Turn and Burn

The Development of Coal Mining and the Railways in the North East of England

Mike Leddra

University of Sunderland Press

© Mike Leddra

ISBN 978-1-906832-00-1

First Published 2008

Cover Design Bradley O'Mahoney Creative Ltd

Published in Great Britain by
The University of Sunderland Press
in association with Business Education Publishers Limited
evolve Business Centre
Cygnet Way
Rainton Bridge Business Park
Houghton-le-Spring
Tyne & Wear
DH4 5QY

Tel: 0191 3055160
Fax: 0191 3055506

British Cataloguing-in-Publications Data
A catalogue record for this book is available from the British Library

Printed in Great Britain by Alden

Ann, Philippa, Stuart and Adam

Contents

Illustrations

Maps

Illustrations

Photographs

Preface

This book grew out of a request by a couple of teachers for 'two pages of information on coal mining and railways in our area', to use with their pupils. The more information I collected the more involved the story became, and it was soon obvious that a simple two-page fact sheet would actually do the incredible history of the area and its people an injustice.

I have tried as hard as possible to cross-check all the information that has been included, which on occasions proved more difficult than expected. For many 'well known facts' there are a number of alternatives, and trying to sort out fact from fiction sometimes proved difficult. In some cases therefore I have included what appears to be the most reliable version, which other people may disagree with. All I can say is that I have tried my best and I hope you enjoy it; it certainly makes an interesting story with some unexpected twists and turns.

Finally I would like to explain why I chose the title *Turn and Burn*. I thought it encompassed the essence and energy of the two subject areas. I also have to admit that beyond geology, geography and history my main love is old aeroplanes and the term 'turn and burn' refers to a jet flying on reheat.

I hope you enjoy reading this as much as I have enjoyed writing it.

Mike Leddra
August 2008

Acknowledgements

This book could not have been written without the help of a number of people. These include Paul Cowell, who effectively instigated the whole thing when, as a teacher at Biddick School, he asked if I could put together a couple of pages on coal mining in the local area for their pupils. His enthusiasm together with Joe Small and Simon Emsley at St. Roberts of Newmister School helped to drive this forward.

I would like to say a very big thank you to Cat, Paul, Carly, Caroline, Janine and Karen, my former colleagues at the University of Sunderland, who had to put up with a frequent bombardment of questions such as 'What do you think of this?', 'Do you know anything about that?', 'Does this makes sense?' and 'Can you check the English for me?'

Thank you also to Andy Lane and Bill Scott, both former colleagues in geology at the University of Sunderland, for helping and showing me so much of the local geology over the last fourteen years. They have been an inspiration not only to me but to all of our former geology students that we have had the privilege of teaching over the years.

I am grateful to Tom Lancastle for inspiring me to study geology and geography, along with the late Prof. Jake Hancock who ignited my enthusiasm for the combination of geology and history which, with geography, should never be separated.

For their help with some of the mining information, I thank Brian Young and Dave Lawrence at the British Geological Survey as well as John Ball and Rob Jones for their fantastic help with local information.

To my family, Ann, Philippa, Stuart and Adam, I am grateful for their patience when being dragged around numerous sites to take photographs or 'encouraged' to take walks along tracks and bridleways whilst I tried to explain to them how exciting it was to walk in the footsteps of history. They also had to put up with having to look at all the photographs I'd taken after every trip, and long nights waiting to get on the computer to finish homework etc. whilst I 'just finished this bit'.

I express immense gratitude to my mum, dad and twin sister for all the times they encouraged me when we were younger, by taking us to so many interesting places, and firing-up my imagination for geology, geography and history.

Finally, I would like to express special thanks to our Philippa for her patience in reading through this and suggesting the final changes.

Chapter 1

Geology of the Coalfields

Three things are required in mining: an ability to reach the coal seams; an ability to transport the coal and finally a market for it. As each of these has changed over time, the North East has been in a particularly good position to take a leading role in most aspects of the development of the coal industry. The nature of the countryside and the location of the coalfield with regard to the main rivers and the coastline meant that coal mining and the development of the railways went hand-in-hand in the North East of England and in the east Durham area in particular. As demand increased, new methods of mining and transporting the coal were introduced which took it from being a local activity to a national and even an international one. For this reason it is acknowledged that the North East is the oldest intensive mining area in the country.

However, to be able to appreciate how mining and the railways developed we need to have a basic understanding of the layout and geology of the coalfield (figure 1). The geology of our area comprises rocks from two different geological periods, the Carboniferous and the Permian. It was during these two periods that the coal seams, limestones and sandstones, which form such an important part of the story of coal mining and the development of the railways in North East England, were formed. These two periods take us back a significant distance into earth history, back to between 345 and 225 million years ago. Back then, the earth look significantly different compared to its appearance today; all of the land-masses were grouped together in to two large continents, a northern one which has been named Laurussia or a southern one called Gondwana.

A number of smaller microplates, including Avalonia, which contained England, and Wales, had previously broken away from the northern edge of Gondwana and had

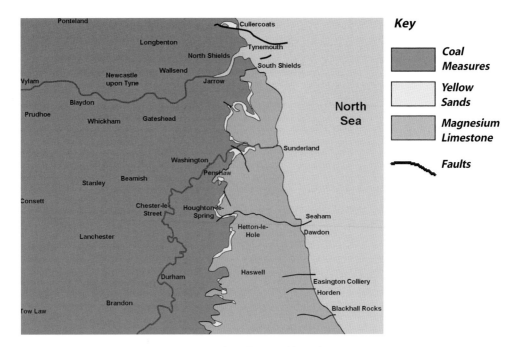

Figure 1: General geology and location map

come crashing into the southern edge of Laurussia. In fact, within a global setting, Avalonia had hit Laurussia producing the Caledonian Mountains of Scotland and Ireland, and then another microplate, named Armorican, which had also been making steady progress northwards, ran in to the southern margin of Avalonia. This collision, termed the Variscan Orogeny, resulted in the formation of a large mountain range, equivalent in size to the Himalayas, which stretched from Russia in the east across southern Europe, through Devon and Cornwall, to North America, which at the time, was still part of the European continent. The collision also led to the formation of a single super-continent named Pangaea, which comprised all the continents we have today and almost stretched from pole to pole. Although, as we shall see below, the rocks of North East England indicate hot tropical conditions, those on the southern continents tell us that, at the time, much of the earth was suffering climatically cold conditions with extensive glaciers equivalent to those of the last glaciations.

How can this be? It is important to realise that the continents are not fixed in one position, but move slowly around the surface of the earth. When the older rocks of the two period were being laid down, Britain was located on or just to the north of the Equator, so although much of the earth was gripped by a significant cold period (termed Ice House conditions), we were benefiting from a warm, tropical climate. Over time, we have, and still are drifting northwards, a fact that is reflected in the nature of the rocks beneath our feet. Towards the end of the Carboniferous Period and the start of the Permian Period, our northwards drift took us out of the tropical belt and in to drier conditions of the Trade Wind Belt, a change which is reflected in the rocks.

The Carboniferous Period, which is the older of the two geological periods, lasted from 345 to 280 million years ago but only the youngest part of the sequence of rocks deposited during this period are important in our story. These are known as the Coal Measures and, as the name implies contains all the important coal seams that were exploited by the coal mines. The coal seams, of which there are more than twenty formed in a cyclic sequence of mudstones, siltstones, sandstones and coals. Most coal seams are approximately 0.5m thick although some may be up to 3m deep. They vary not only in thickness but also in quality so that individual seams may not be workable throughout the area.

At the time the coal seams were formed the North East was a relatively flat, low-lying area with mountains to the South and North, and a sea to the East. In fact the area was covered by a large delta fed by rivers which bought large amounts of sands and clays that were being eroded from the North-East and West. The large numbers of fossil trees and leaves found in the coal seams show that the area was covered with a thick peat bog which grew in a warm, humid environment. When the trees and other vegetation died, they often fell in water which prevented them from rotting. It is this preserved vegetation that, after burial beneath other rocks formed the coal seams that were so important to not only the wealth and development of North East England, but to the entire country.

The Coal Measures are overlain to the East by a sequence of sandstones, mudstones, limestones, dolomites, and evaporites deposited during the Permian Period between 280 and 225 million years ago. The oldest, Permian rocks which lie directly on top of the Coal Measures comprise a sequence of sandstones known as the Yellow Sands. These comprise a sequence of large-scale sand dunes, deposited in a wide-spread, desert which are fairly weak and highly porous and permeable (i.e. they can hold large amounts of water which can easily flow through them). This desert is thought to be one of the largest in earth history, and the structure of the dunes can readily be seen in places such as Cullercoats (figure 2) and Claxheugh Rock. They indicate that as Britain moved northwards it moved in to, what we would regard today as the Trade Wind Belt. This, together with effects of the growing mountains to the South, resulted in a significantly drier climate than that experienced during the Carboniferous Period. Further changes were to occur as the sea rapidly invaded the desert, depositing first a thin layer of mudstone, known as the Marl Slate, between the sand dunes, which is renowned for the fossil fish it contains, and then a deeper water sequence of limestones and dolomites (magnesium limestones). These limestones and dolomites, which together are known as the Magnesian Limestone, formed a reef and a lagoon equivalent to the Great Barrier Reef off the Eastern coast of Australia. Although both rock types show significant variations in strength, the limestones are generally stronger than the dolomites. The other point of interest with regard to coal mining, is that as the limestones and dolomites filled in the gaps between the desert sand dunes before covering them completely, their thickness varies considerably across the buried coalfield, a fact which, as we shall see, caused significant problems to the coal miners.

Generally all the rocks dip (tilt) downwards at an angle of approximately 5° towards the coast. The stronger Permian sequence forms an escarpment with a relatively flat surface which has been modified by later glacial activity. Although both sequences of rocks are cut by a number of faults these tend to have only small vertical displacements.

The only large fault in the area is a large boundary fault known as the Ninety Fathom Fault which is exposed along the coast at Cullercoats, between Tynemouth and Whitley Bay (figure 2).

Figure 2: The Ninety Fathom Fault (represented by the dashed line) exposed at the coast at Cullercoats

The coal field reaches the surface in the north and west and dips gently downwards under the Permian Magnesian Limestone before continuing out to sea. This explains why the earliest and shallowest mines are found west of the Permian escarpment close to the main rivers where the coal seams are close to the surface and the modern deep mines were located on the Permian rocks along the coast where they exist at significant depths. As mining moved out from the rivers new economic and efficient methods of transporting the coal had to be found. This expansion also meant that alternative methods of mining had to be introduced to be able to reach increasingly deeper coal seams. This was reliant on improvements in ventilation and drainage. Once it had been established that the coal measures continued eastwards under the Permian escarpment even more sophisticated methods of mining were required. This ultimately resulted in the more recent collieries mining coal up to eight miles (12.9km) out under the North Sea.

At each point on this journey, the miners either had to embrace new technologies if they existed or wait until they had developed enough to be able to use them. It is often said that necessity is the mother of invention and this is particularly true in the Durham and Northumberland coalfields. The story also involves its own fair share of politics, greed and shady dealing all of which added an extra dimension to the growth of the coal industry.

As you would expect, given the history of mining in North East England, this can only be a review and not a comprehensive study. This review was bourn out of a request for teaching materials designed to give students an overview of how mining and the railways developed in the area. There also appeared to be a scarcity of preserved mining and railway artefacts which seemed rather odd given that they formed such an important part of the local and national history.

Chapter 2

Early Coal Mining to 1700

The Romans may well have mined and used coal in our area as coal cinders have been found at some Roman sites. Some of the earliest recorded mining can be found at Escomb, where mining was recorded during the twelfth century. One of the first industrial uses of coal was for glass-making, which started in the Sunderland area. Most early mining, however, developed around Newcastle and Gateshead where the coal was close to the surface, or in the banks of the River Tyne. 'Coal smiths', who traded coal, were already established at Bishopwearmouth and Sedgefield by 1180 and in Newcastle by 1239, the year that Henry III granted the Port of Newcastle the rights to dig coal. In 1183 a coal mine at Escomb was producing coal for the iron works at Coundon.

Large scale mining, under the control of the monks in Durham, really began in the thirteenth century with the establishment of mines at Cockfield, Coundon, Hett, Lanchester, Ferryhill, Lumley and Rainton. These early mines used two different methods of mining. The first used tunnels known as 'adits', levels or drifts (the preferred term in the North East) which were dug into the coal seams where they were exposed in river banks and the sides of hills (figures 3-5).

Figure 3: (Above Left) Entrance of an adit mine at Blists HIll Open Air Museum, Shropshire

Figure 4: (Above) Inside the adit at Beamish Open Air Museum

Figure 5: Entrance to the adit mine at Beamish Open Air Museum

If the coal was just below the surface a second method was employed called bell pitting. As the name suggests these were holes which were bell-shaped in cross-section (figure 6). The miners dug a shaft down to the coal seam and then dug outwards around the shaft until they thought that the ground may become unstable. They then moved along the seam, dug an adjacent Bell Pit and continued to do this until they had retrieved as much of the coal as possible. It has said that by 1256 it was becoming difficult to travel along the road between Corbridge and Newcastle at night because of the possibility of falling in to one of the pits!

Figure 6: A block diagram showing a series of bell pits

Originally coal was transported locally or to the coal staithes built along the rivers on pack horses or in two-wheeled carts called 'Cowps'. As demand increased, coal had to be carried in larger amounts, and four-wheeled wagons or 'Wains' were introduced. These were pulled by two horses. These were often used on special 'Wainroads' which were only used for colliery traffic. Early wainroads ran from Whickham along what are now Coalway Lane, Dunston Road and Ravensworth Road.

Most of the coal at this time was transported by hand carts or horses along 'wain' roads. As coal was relatively heavy and the conditions of these roads were often little better than muddy tracks, the coal could only be transported over short distances. This was all right if the coal happened to be close to the place where it was to be used, but local use was limited. This was of course before the industrial revolution, when demand for coal was to increase significantly. The only reliable way of transporting coal over longer distances was along the local rivers. This meant that most mining was still generally confined to the areas around the major rivers. The map shows that the majority of the mines were clustered around the River Tyne in the Blaydon, Gateshead, Whickham and Winlaton area, although mines were also established around Blyth (figure 7).

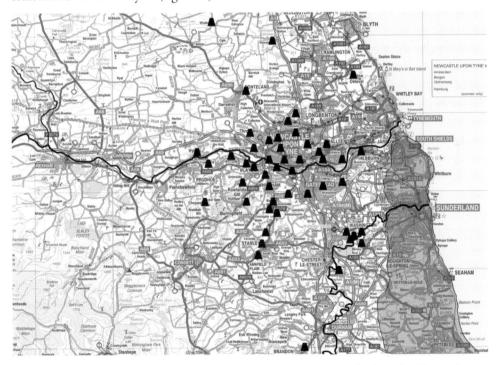

Figure 7: Pre 1700 coal mines. (Note the shaded area represents the Permian Magnesian Limestone which lie over the Carboniferous Coal Measures)

Around 1303 the monks at Finchale Abbey were thought to be the first people to produce coal from mines below the level of natural water drainage, because they had installed a pump at Moorhouse. In 1305 Thomas Migg made the first recorded export of coal from the North East to London. The use of coal in London had obviously increased significantly, as in 1306 a petition was presented to King Edward I which aimed to prevent the use of coal because of the 'sulphurous smoke' it generated. The petitions did not succeed because by this time the amount of wood available for heating and cooking had decreased to such an extent that there was no alternative to the use of coal.

The area of coal production continued to increase and by 1315 there were mines at Cullercoats and Cowpen. Prior to the 1350s the Bishop of Durham, who owned most of the land from which coal was being mined, had effective control of most of the mining. Newcastle was gaining in importance, particularly with regard to transporting and exporting on the Tyne so much that in 1334 King Edward had to ban the Mayor and bailiffs of Newcastle from mooring their ships on the Gateshead (Durham) side of the river.

Increasing demand meant that mining began to spread further away from the banks of the rivers. For example there was mining at Gateshead (in 1344), Lumley (by 1349) and Rainton (in 1354). Five coal mines had also been established around Whickham with others at Ferryhill, Hett and Lanchester by 1356 and a set of staithes had been constructed at Pipewellgate in 1349.

Coal was used in a number of early industries including the production of salt and pottery, lime for building, soap boiling, brewing, glass and paper making and the smelting of iron. Some of this was on a significant scale. There were salt pans, for example, at Seaton Delaval as early as 1408 and at Seaton Sluice in 1564 and the salt industry at South Shields was even larger. In fact by 1767 the salt industry at North and South Shields was using around one thousand tons of coal a year. In 1511 a coal mine opened at Offerton to supply coal to the salt pans in Sunderland, and the smiths at Sedgefield and Monkwearmouth also used coal rather than wood.

In 1357 the Burgesses of Newcastle were granted a royal licence to dig coal on the Town Moor. Mining also started at Cockfield prior to 1375, in Heworth in 1376 and at Evenwood in 1383. By 1380 there were 118 ships exporting coal from Newcastle to 39 different, foreign ports. Coal was becoming an increasingly important trade and the merchants in Newcastle tried to claim sole rights to be able to ship coal from the Tyne. In 1530 an Act of Parliament granted their wishes and effectively gave them a monopoly on the export of coal from the area. In fact Edward III had already decreed in 1344 that all the coal produced by the Bishops of Durham should pass through the Port of Tyne. At that time the coal mines at Whickham were the largest in Europe.

Control of the production and export of coal was to remain a contentious issue as most coal was being produced from areas around the southern, Gateshead side of the river on land owned by the Bishop of Durham which the Newcastle merchants also wanted to control. Until then the monks had kept strict control over the amount of coal that was being produced, and they were then able to restrict the growth in production and therefore control prices. But things were about to change!

During the sixteenth century, as wood available for burning began to run out in London and southern England, the demand for coal increased. The Durham coalfield, with its location close to the east coast and with good communications via the rivers, was able to meet this demand. But control of coal production and its export continued to be a contentious issue. Most of the coal was being produced from Gateshead and other areas south of the Tyne on land owned by the Bishop of Durham. In fact in the 1580s most of the coal was being produced from as few as 20 to 25 collieries. Coal export, however, was controlled by the merchants in Newcastle.

Newcastle had taken control of the whole of the Newcastle Bridge because they claimed that a lack of maintenance of the Durham section was adversely affecting their trade. But in 1415 the Bishop of Durham persuaded the King to force the Mayor of Newcastle to hand back Durham's third of the Bridge. This resulted in a power struggle between the merchants, monks and bishops which remained unresolved for the next 150 years. This included the period of the Protestant Reformation, when the area around Gateshead was taken away from the monks and put under the control of Newcastle. This freed coal production from the restrictions imposed by the monks and bishops until Queen Mary restored the land to the Durham. When Queen Elizabeth I came to the throne she also allowed the Bishops of Durham to retain ownership, which enabled them to lease the mining rights to other people (see below).

In 1609, 239,261 tons (243,089 tonnes) of coal were exported from the Tyne and 11,648 tons (11, 834 tonnes) from the Wear. In 1615 there were 200 ships exporting coal from the Tyne to London and a further 200 exporting it to the rest of the country. It was probably this increase in shipping that led to the development of ship-building in the area. In fact James Cook worked on Whitby colliers supplying coal from Tyne and Wear to London in 1746.

As the easily-accessible coal began to run out the mine owners had to move further inland. This meant that they had to change their mining methods, as they needed to dig deeper to find the coal. It also meant that they had to transport the coal over longer distances, so they needed to find alternative methods of transporting the coal. As the distances between mines and the staithes increased it also became more cost-effective to move the coal in larger quantities. This meant the mines had to increase the size of the wagons they used. They could no longer rely on using hand carts. Prior to this they had been able to use low-quality mud tracks which were usually impassable in the winter and often out of actions for much of the spring and autumn. During this period mines opened in Whitley, Hartley, Amble and Bilton.

To meet the increase in demand the local coal industry also had to change from a less *ad hoc* activity to a more organised, structured, mechanised, better financed and skills-based industry. This in effect led to an early Industrial Revolution in the North East, ahead of the rest of the country. In fact the first 'deep mines' using shallow shafts were being dug as early as the fourteenth century Coal was also an important requirement for the glass industry because the use of wood for glass-making had been banned in 1615. The glass industry was so important to the region that by the 1740s Tyneside was the main producer of window glass in the country.

Even so, until the seventeenth century coal was generally only used for heating and other household purposes. The English Civil War (1642-1651) also led to a further expansion of mining, and pits were dug along the banks of the River Wear around Fatfield, where the first shaft is thought to have been dug as early as 1618. Other mines were established out towards Carterthorne, Etherley, Harraton, Offerton, Lumley and Tanfield.

As mines became deeper, concern over mine safety and the number of miners dying in accidents led to 2,000 miners signing a petition which was delivered to parliament calling for improved ventilation in the mines.

Formation of the Mining Cartels

The right to mine coal to the south of the Tyne appears to have been included in a 'Great Lease' as early as 1458, when it was purchased by Sir William Eure. It probably included a similar area to that of the 'Grand Lease' which covered the Manors of Gateshead and Whickham. This was the most profitable coal mining area at the time when Queen Elizabeth I bought the 'Grand Lease' from the Bishop of Durham in 1582. She set it for a term of 79 years and passed it on to Lord Leicester, who granted it to one of his friends, Thomas Sutton the Master of the Ordnance at Berwick. But because he was not a Freeman of the City he was effectively excluded from trading his coal through the port of Newcastle which eventually led him to sell the lease. He increased it to a 99-year lease and then sold it to Henry Anderson and William Selby, who bought it on behalf of the Burgesses of Newcastle in 1583 using town funds. (They had previously tried to take over coal production in the area after Bishop Pilkington of Durham died in 1576.) The burgesses, who were Freemen of the city and also known as the Hostmen's Corporation of Freemen, were the only people allowed to ship coal on the River Tyne. This effectively gave them a stranglehold on the movement of coal in the area as early as 1547, because they acted as the middlemen between the coal merchants and the coal buyers. The term 'host' derives from their position of looking after buyers when they came to the city.

This group became so influential that they dominated Newcastle politics at the time and an 'inner circle' of about twenty, who were the most powerful Hostmen, was known as the 'Lords of coal'. These were exclusively members of the Merchant Adventurers, who held virtually all of the key posts in local government. The Hostmen were so powerful that they were granted a charter in 1600 as the Fraternity of Hostmen of Newcastle, which re-enforced their dominance of the coal trade. However, it should be noted that by this time there was also a large group of mine owners who were not Freemen of Newcastle and were therefore not part of the Hostmen. This group was sufficiently large that the Hostmen could not ignore them.

When collieries such as the ones at Wallsend opened on the seaward side of the Tyne Bridge, it meant that the Keelmen (part of the Hostmen), who owned the Keels (the small flat-bottomed boats) used to transport coal from the staithes upstream of the bridge to the loading areas on the seaward side gradually lost their control and power. Trade decreased so much that eventually they ceased to exist. Until this period, coal production was generally a seasonal activity with coal being mined and transported to the staithes during the better weather. The mine owners used to store sufficient coal at the staithes so that it could continue to be shipped out when mining closed down for the winter. The coal was usually stored under cover to protect it from deterioration in bad weather.

During the English Civil War Parliament placed an embargo on the coal trade from the Port of Tyne. This caused mining in the area to go through a period of decline which also weakened the Hostmen's control and influence. Following the Civil War the Hostmen split into three different groups. One group, the Keelmen, ran the keel boat traffic on the Tyne. A second group controlled the marketing of the coal, and there was a third group who were mine owners. Eventually the last group, who were powerful local landowners, formed a cartel in the early seventeenth century called the 'Coal Office Newcastle' under the leadership of Sir Henry Liddell. This group was formed to try to bring stability to coal production in the area and to try to control the amount of coal being produced and exported to London. They produced an agreement known as the 'Limitation of the Vend' which was designed to restrict the amount of coal being produced, so as to maintain a high price and ensure that no mine owners could make a profit at another owner's expense. The number of people in the 'vend' varied from 29 in 1603 to 48 in 1617.

The ship owners, whose boats transported the coal to London, felt that these restrictions were hurting their trade. Eventually, following a boycott, they convinced the Privy Council in London to issue a warrant which forced the mine owners to allow the free trade of coal. In 1708 there was a further attempt to regulate output, but this had broken down by 1715 due to cheating and internal arguments.

Finally a group which comprised Sir Henry Liddell (Lord Ravensworth) and Colonel George Liddell, The Honourable Sidney and Edward Wortley-Montague, George Bowes and Thomas Ord formed the Grand Alliance Company on the 27 June 1726. This group, which was generally known as the 'Grand Allies' formed one of the most significant partnerships with regard to the development of mining in Northumberland and Durham.

On formation of the Alliance it took over ownership of the 'Grand Lease', which, when its 99-year term ran out in 1681 had been granted to Colonel Liddell and his partners by the then Bishop of Durham, Bishop Crewe. This meant that as soon as the Alliance was formed it owned almost half of the collieries in the area.One of the main reasons for establishing the Grand Alliance was to enable its members to have free passage for their coal across each others' land and therefore avoid the huge cost of paying wayleaves. As early as 1696 it had been suggested that Parliament should regulate the prices landowners could change for wayleaves, as it was thought that the high prices could lead to the closure of some pits, which would lead to a decrease in coal exports.

It appears that membership of the 'Grand Lease' included mine owners other than the Grand Allies. These included the Riddles of Gateshead, Henry Maddison, William Hall, Sir Nicholas Tempest, Sir George Vane, the Russells of Brancepeth and the Brandlings of Gosforth (see Middleton Railway). This allowed the members to spread the cost of building waggonways and to develop collieries which were too large for any individual mine owner to develop. As with the other attempts to regulate production this began to break down in the 1760s and by 1771 yet another 'Limitation of Vend' was initiated, but this only lasted until 1830. There were other partnerships which tried to compete with the 'Grand Allies' in different areas of the coal field such as the Newcastle Hostmen who controlled the Tyneside collieries, and a group comprising Sir John Clavering and the Mallabar family who owned pits in the west of the coalfield.

Chapter 3

Mining from 1700: Construction of the Waggonways and the Introduction of Steam

With the start of the eighteenth century, as urbanisation increased and the industrial revolution began, the export of coal increased significantly. In 1704, 473,080 tons (480,650 tonnes) of coal were exported from Newcastle and 174,264 tons 177,052 tonnes) were exported from Sunderland. But by 1750 this had increased to almost 1.2 million tons (1.22 million tonnes) from the two ports, which at the time accounted for nearly half of the entire country's coal production.

It was during this period, as mine workings extended to greater depths and further from the shaft, that the problem of 'fire damp' and explosions began to increase. The first 'mine disaster' explosion occurred at the Stoney Flat Colliery, Gateshead in 1705 where 29 men and one woman were killed. This was followed by an explosion at Fatfield in 1708 which killed 69 people (figure 8), Bensham (1743) with 80 deaths, Fatfield again in 1767 (39 killed), Chartershaugh (in Fatfield) 1773 with 23 dead and Picktree (1794) which killed 30 miners.

To help to prevent the build-up of mine gas, different methods for ventilating the mines were introduced. For example, a ventilation furnace was used at the bottom of the shaft at Long Benton Colliery from 1749, and at Wallsend 'B' Pit from 1786. A surface furnace and an 'air tube' were used at North Biddick Colliery from 1756 and a fire basket, used for ventilation, was first introduced at Fatfield in the 1750s.

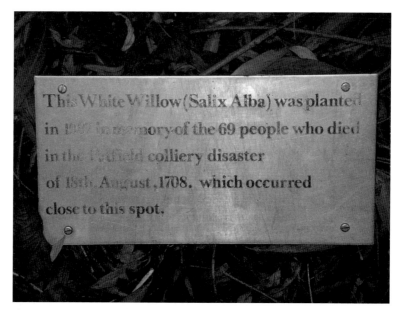

Figure 8: Commemorative sign to those killed in the 1708 accident at Fatfield

Changes were also introduced to the methods of mining, to increase ventilation. John Buddle introduced the panel system of mining in the Wallsend 'C' Pit in 1810. This meant that the coal was mined in distinct districts, which were surrounded by coal barriers. This method reduced surface subsidence and allowed better air circulation through better control of the ventilation furnaces. The first use of pillar and stall mining, where pillars of coal are left intact to support the roof of the mining workings, is thought to have been at Chartershaugh (Fatfield) in 1738. This method of mining, which continued until the twentieth century, allowed miners to dig out significantly more coal than previous methods. At the same colliery Michael Menzies invented a machine in 1753 which could be used to bring coal to the surface.

Most of the mines were still confined, or relatively close, to the major rivers in the area (figure 9).

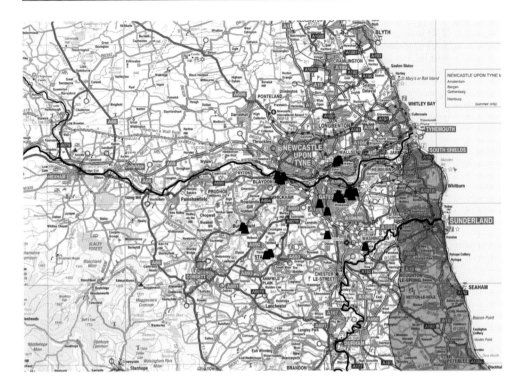

Figure 9: Locations of major coal mines dug between 1700 and 1750

Early Waggonways

By 1689 the mines along the banks of the Tyne began to run out of coal or were flooded, so mining had to move further inland. This meant that a more efficient method of transporting coal was required. Wooden waggonways were developed that used oak tracks on which carts could be pulled either by people or, more usually, by horses. (The term waggon with two g's was introduced to identify waggons that were used on rails and hence the name waggonway also has two g's.) Although waggonways were expensive to build they allowed horses to pull more than one cart at a time and therefore increased efficiency and productivity. They also proved to be more reliable, as often mining had to stop during the winter when the roads and tracks became too muddy to allow heavy loads of coal to be moved about. The first recorded waggonway in the UK was built at Wollaton in Northamptonshire in 1603.

The first three waggonways in the North East were built around 1605 for pits at Bedlington, Bebside and Cowpen, to take coal to the River Blyth (see figure 10). These mines were owned by Huntington Beaumont (and Peter Delavel who owned the land), who had used flanged, wheeled waggons in his mines in Nottingham before moving to Blyth. He could not compete with the Newcastle Hostmen, struggled to make a profit and eventually gave up and moved back to Nottinghamshire in

1614. The waggonways closed in 1618. This effectively took away any incentive to build other waggonways in the area except for the Plessey Waggonway (figure 10) which was built between Plessey Hall Farm and Blyth, a distance of 5.5 miles (8.8km) in 1709. This closed in 1812. The first waggonway built to take coal to the Tyne was not constructed until 1649 at Whickham. In 1671 Sir Thomas Liddell built a waggonway from his mine at Ravensworth to Dunston which was known as the Team Way (figure 11). Some sources also state that Liddell built the first Tyneside waggonway, from Teams Colliery to Derwenthaugh, as early as 1630.

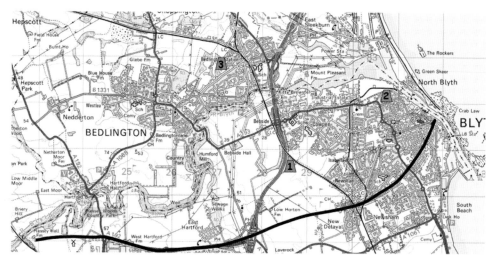

Figure 10: Route of the Plessey Waggonway and the approximate locations of the early collieries at Bebside (1), Cowpen (2) and Bedlington (3)

Figure 10(a): A view along part of the Plessey Waggonway east of the A192

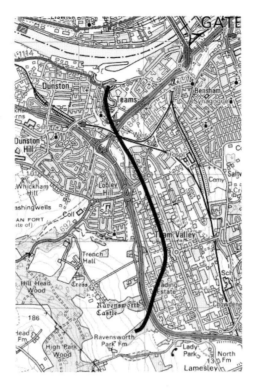

Figure 11: The line represents the route of the Team Way Waggonway

Building waggonways could only be afforded by the owners of the larger pits, who could then transport their coal down in larger horse-drawn waggons called Chaldrons, to coal staithes along the river banks. This coal was referred to as 'seasale' coal, because it was then transferred to ships for markets along the east and south coasts. The smaller pits which could not afford to build waggonways were restricted to selling their coal to local users, and therefore this coal was called 'landsale' coal.

Prior to 1750, most of the waggonways led to the south bank of the Tyne or the north bank of the Wear, at Fatfield (see figure 46). In fact, the map showing where all the new mines were built between 1700 and 1750 clearly shows this, with mines radiating out from the Tyne in particular. From 1750 to 1800 waggonways were also built on the north bank of the Tyne. By this time there were approximately 150 miles (240km) of waggonways in the North East, which accounted for almost half of all the waggonways in the country. In fact, they were so commonly associated with this area that waggonways were often called 'Newcastle Roads'.

As the coal that could be retrieved by drift mining began to run out the mine owners had to switch to 'deep mining', where the miners had to dig a shaft down to the coal seams. They then dug along the coal seams using the pillar and stall mining technique. 'Deep mining' involved a significant jump in technology. Not only did the miners have to dig the shafts before they could get to the coal but the coal and everything else that went into or came out of the mine had to be lifted up and down the shaft.

This also involved a significant increase in the costs of constructing and running the mines, which many small mine owners could not afford. During the 1720s and 1730s collieries opened at Byker, Jesmond, Heaton, Wylam and Longbenton.

One of the most important sites in the story of waggonways and railways is Wylam, on the north bank of the Tyne approximately 9 miles (14.5km) West of Newcastle. In about 1748 Wylam Colliery was linked by a five-mile (8km) long waggonway to carry coal to the staithes at Lemington, which was the most westerly point that coal keels (barges) could come up the Tyne to collect coal (figure 12). These then carried the coal to the staithes further down the Tyne, from where it could be transferred to larger ships. At the time the original Tyne Bridge acted as a barrier to larger ships sailing up the Tyne, so the staithes were all located downstream of the bridge. There were two other waggonways in the area which linked Lemington to the collieries at Holywell Main and Greenwich Moor (Black Callerton) and Throckley and Wallbottle (figure 13). Each waggon required a horse and a man to control it, which made the waggonways very labour intensive and expensive to run, particularly with regard to the cost of keeping and feeding the horses. It is thought that a journey of 6 miles (9.6km) added about 60 per cent to the cost of coal production.

Figure 12: Eastern end of the Wylam Waggonway at Newburn

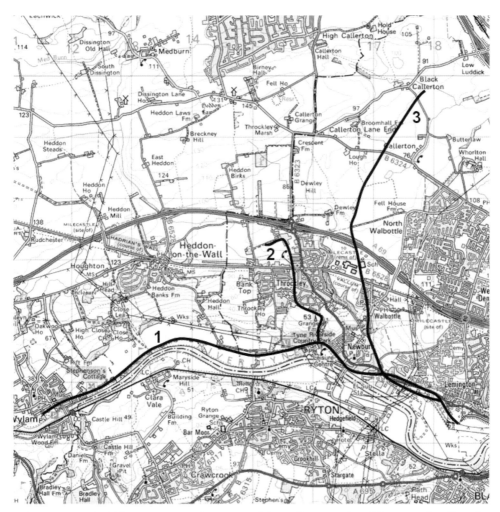

Figure 13: The bold lines represent the routes of the Wylham (1), Throckley (2) and Wallbottle (3) waggonways

During the clearing of the Lampton Coke Works site, 1560m of wooden (oak) waggonways were uncovered, consisting of four nearly complete tracks and sections of six others which were built between 1789 and 1791 (figure 14). These are thought to be the oldest existing wooden tracks in the world. They also have two sets of points, but oddly enough there appears to be no evidence that the waggons were pulled by horses! It has been proposed that when clearing and restoration of the site is complete a museum building will be constructed around these to preserve and display them. Another site, at Rainton Bridge, was excavated in 2001 and 2002. Although there were no tracks found at this site, the track beds and trackside ditches still existed. These indicated that there were two waggonways that led to North Pit and two which may have gone to another shaft to the south (figure 15). These were probably built around 1717 and operated as a line which took loaded coal waggons to the staithes on the River Wear and another that was used to bring the empty waggons back.

Figure 14: Site of the wooden waggonway at the former Lambton Coke Works

Figure 15: This embankment is throught to be part of the 1717 waggonway at Rainton

Waggonways were usually constructed with a base layer of stone, ash or coal ballast on which the wooden sleepers were laid. There were two sets of rails, a bottom set made from pine or fur overlaid by another set made from hard wood such as oak, beech or, sycamore (figure 16). The wood was usually imported from locations in southern England such as Sussex or the New Forest. The wooden rails were secured to the sleepers by wooden pegs and a layer of finer ballast was added in between and around the rails. This brought the surface almost up to the top of the rails to make it easier for horses and people to walk on. Finally shallow drainage ditches were added on either side to try to keep the waggonway dry. One of the advantages of having two sets of rails was that when the first set wore down they could be removed and the waggons could run on the second set, which reduced the cost and frequency of having to re-lay the rails. The first wooden rails used underground in the region were laid from East Kenton to Scotswood in 1778 and water from the mine was allowed to drain down either side of the waggonway.

Figure 16: A reproduction coal waggon and section of wooden track at Causey Arch

Tanfield Railway and Causey Arch

Waggonways were built across private land and the mine owners had to pay the landowners a wayleave (a type of land use tax) to allow them to transport coal across their land. Some of the landowners, realising they had a 'captive market', continuously increased their wayleaves until they were charging significant sums of money. This may have been one of the reasons why the 'Grand Allies' (see Ch.2 p.11) were effectively a cartel set up to protect their mining interests. They had opened mines around Dipton, Pontop, Tanfield and Tantobie and built the first section of the Tanfield Waggonway by about 1632. When the 'Grand Allies', wanted to build a waggonway from their pits at Tanfield and Causey to the banks of the Tyne they decided to choose a new route which would be shorter, more level and would avoid some of the landowners who had been charging them increasingly more expensive wayleaves. The new route required some major engineering including a huge embankment and a stone bridge. The bridge was built in 1725 and collapsed soon afterwards! A second bridge was then built at a cost of £2,000. This bridge, known as Causey Arch (and Dawson's Bridge), had a single arch with a span of 105 feet (32m) and was the largest of its kind in the world for the next 30 years (figures 17 and 17(a)).

Figure 17: A side of Causey Arch

Figure 17(a): A view of the top of Causey Arch

The waggonway itself was also a rarity at the time it was constructed as it had two sets of tracks: the 'mainway' which carried loaded coal waggons to the staithes, and the 'byeway' which carried empty ones back to the pits. Tanfield Railway, which developed from this waggonway, is now the oldest working railway in the world (figure 18) and Causey Arch is the world's oldest railway bridge!

Figures 18: (Above and Right) The Tanfield Railway

Figure 18(a): The bridleway that follows the line of the Tanfield Railway down in to Team Valley

Expansion of the Waggonways

As mining continued to develop further inland, other waggonways were built. A consortium of Lord Windsor, Lord Dunkerron, Matthew Ridley and John Simpson built a line from their collieries at Pontop, Pontop Pike and Bushblades via Rowland's Gill and Swalwell to the staithes at Derwenthaugh. The 'Grand Allies' also extended the Tanfield Waggonway to Beamish South Moor. In 1671 Sir Thomas Liddell built a waggonway from his Ravensworth Colliery to the staithes at Dunston. Sir John Claverigg and Thomas Brumell built a waggonway from their Litz and Buck's Nook collieries over Tanfield Moor in 1712 which George Pitt used when he developed his mines at Tanfield.

But what about the Wearside area? Before 1812 when they started building long waggonways, all the lines came down to the river around Fatfield on the North and West side of Cox Green/Mount Pleasant, on the South and East of the River Wear, where the coal was loaded on to small keels boats to be transported down stream to Sunderland. The first waggonway was probably the Flatts, or Allen's Waggonway, built around 1693 to bring coal from pits to the north west of Chester-le-Street to the River Wear at Fatfield. By 1710 the 'Dean Hedworths' Waggonway had been built which brought coal from the Pelton area, and there may have been one from the Washington area as well. The Flatts Line was extended to reach Pelton and Hedworth and ran parallel to a line from Beamish. Another went to Usworth, Birtley and Harraton. Washington also had a waggonway which went north to the River Tyne at Pelaw.

Figure 19: Examples of canals in Chester and Stoke

But why did the North East move towards the continued growth of waggonways and the eventual development of the railways when the other coal fields around the country were building canals to solve the same problems? The mines in the North East were fortunate because they were close to the coast compared to most of the other coal fields; so long distance transport was by sea. The other land-locked coal fields had to find an efficient method of transporting large volumes of coal over long distances.

The first canal, built in 1776 which did not include a river section was the Bridgewater Canal. This was designed by James Brindley for the Duke of Bridgewater to transport coal from his collieries in Worsley to the centre of Manchester. This started the rapid expansion of the canal system which continued until the mid 1830s.

So, why didn't canals catch on in our area? They were proposed and in fact a small section of one was actually built. George Dixon, whose brother Jeremiah is famous for being one of the two surveyors of the Mason-Dixon Line in America, rented the Cockfield Fell Colliery from Sir Henry Vane. George was an engineer, mathematician and chemist who, whilst developing the use of gas for lighting and heating, blew up his house!

Figure 20: The Cockfield canal on the edge of Cockfield Fell

In 1767 he built a short section of canal which he hoped would eventually be extended to the River Tees at Barnard Castle. He met with an influential group which included Edward Pease (the grandfather of the Edward Pease who would become central to the development of the railways), James Backhouse and Sir William Chaytor. Each member of the canal committee donated £50 to the project. They asked James Brindley to design a route that could take coal from the southern part of the Durham Coalfield to the coast. He proposed a 33-mile (53km) long canal which would link Walworth to Yarm. However the plan did not get any further. In 1796 the idea was raised again with the inclusion of a branch that would go all the way to Durham, but again the idea was dropped. It was proposed yet again in 1810 and 1818 but each time got no further.

One of the problems was that the shape of the landscape would have meant the construction of viaducts and up to 50 locks (figure 19) which would have made them very expensive to build and the final route, which closely resembled the original route, would by-pass Darlington. Due to delays in developing the canal it effectively missed the boat because by this time the advent of steam power meant that the existing waggonway network could be developed and expanded using both stationary steam engines and, eventually, locomotives. It is interesting to note that many of the canals around the country ended up in the ownership of railway companies who had a vested interest in seeing coal transport switch from canals to the railways.

The Introduction of Iron Rails

The problem with the wooden tracks used on the waggonways was that they wore out quite quickly, and had to be continuously replaced. The rate of wear increased as the frequency of trips increased, the size and weight of the waggons increased and when iron rims were added to the wooden wheels. Iron rims were invented and then patented by Elias Thornhill's in 1731. Thornhill was a whitesmith in Sunderland who invented a method for making iron wheel rims as well as iron ribs, nuts, bolts and screws which could all be used on the coal waggons.

Mine owners were therefore keen to find other materials that could be used as an alternative to wood, which generally had to be imported from southern England. The introduction of iron rails significantly reduced the problem of wear, but they were far more expensive to make. This meant that yet again only the larger pits could afford them, although their smoother surface meant horses could pull between 30-100 per cent more coal, so the increased efficiency helped to offset the original cost.

The first set of locally-made iron tracks were built at Lawson Main Colliery in Walker in 1797 to take coal waggons from the pit to the staithes on the Tyne. The rails were made of cast iron generally in 4 foot (1.2m) lengths which sat on stone plinths (figures 21 and 22).

Figure 21: Examples of different types of early iron rails at the Stephenson Railway Museum, North Shields

Figure 22: A set of cast iron rails outside the Railway Museum, Darlington

This was 19 years after Abraham D'Arby built the first 'industrial' blast furnace at Coalbrookdale in 1778 and 18 years after the construction of the first iron bridge (D'Arby first smelted iron using coal in 1735). In fact the first iron rails were made at Coalbrookdale in 1767, where the introduction of coke burning blast furnaces led to a significant reduction in the cost of cast iron because these used less coke to provide the same heat than coal fired furnaces (figure 23). The first blast furnace in the North East was built at Lemington in 1797.

Figure 23: The famous Bedlam blast furnace at Ironbridge, Coalbookdale, Shropshire

In 1803 the Surrey Iron Railway, which used wooden rails, was opened between Croydon and Wandsworth. This was the first horse-drawn railway to be built for use by the general public. It was later extended to Merstham in Surrey and was intended to go all the way to Portsmouth to help with transportation of materials for use in the Napoleonic wars, but the idea was abandoned.

Between 1810 and 1830 nearly all of the main routes were converted to iron rails. There were two different designs in use: 'L' shaped 'ledge' or 'plate' tracks, and 'I' shaped rails called 'edge' tracks. At the time most of the country was using 'plate' tracks, but most of the railways in the North East used 'edge' tracks which could carry heavier weights than the 'plate' tracks. Eventually 'edge' tracks became the universal track type. In fact the only main pit/waggonway to use 'ledge' rails in the North East was Wylam Colliery, which played a very important part in the development of steam engines! So what is the difference? Edge rails were used with flat cross sectioned wheels as the rails provided the flange which kept the wheels on the tracks, whereas plate rails were square in cross section and the flanges were on the wheels.

Inclined Planes and Stationary Steam Engines

By 1784 balanced inclines had been introduced on some of the waggonways. These used ropes attached to loaded waggons which ran down the waggonway to pull empty waggons (also attached to the rope) up the incline (slope) to the top of the waggonway. These are sometimes also called ropeways. Most inclined planes (and most waggonways) at the time were single tracks with passing places but some had two tracks. In 1798 Benfield Colliery introduced another system, whereby the waggons were attached to a heavy chain in a shaft at the top of the track. As the loaded waggon went down the waggonway it pulled the chain up the shaft. Once the waggons had been emptied, the weight of the chain compared to the weight of the empty waggons meant that it fell back down the shaft and pulled the waggons back to the top of the waggonway.

Figure 24: Two photographs of the Hay Inclined Plane at the Blists Hill Open Air Museum, Ironbridge, and Shropshire

With the introduction of stationary steam engines, ropeways and inclined planes could be used more efficiently with larger waggons (figure 24). The first stationary steam engine in our area was introduced on a waggonway at Urpeth near Chester-le-Street in 1809 which took coal to staithes on the Tyne. The steam engine powered a huge drum which pulled the waggons along the waggonway. An example of this type of system can be seen at the Bowes Railway, which is the oldest existing standard gauge (the distance between the tracks used by all modern railways) cable haulage railway in the world (figures 25 and 26). The preserved section is the original railway built by George Stephenson in 1826.

Figure 25: The tracks and cable guides at the Bowes Railway

Figure 26: (Left) Shows the difference between an unused section of track, compared to the preserved section in Figure 25: (Above) Shows the inside of one of the cable-winding sheds on the disused section of the Bowes Railway

There is another historic site, Shadons Hill (figure 27), sometimes spelt Shadens Hill, which is a mile (1.6km) south of the railway museum. It was here in the nineteenth century that Durham miners met to create the mineworkers' trade union.

Figure 27: Shadons Hill

With the increasing use of waggonways, inclined planes and ropeways, development of the coal field continued to expand outwards away from the main river valleys. These allowed coal to be transported over larger distances from previously inaccessible areas (with regard to coal mining) to the main coal staithes on the Tyne and Wear.

In particular we see from the 1800 to 1850 map (figure 28) that these opened up a huge area between the rivers Tyne and Wear, as far as Consett in the West, South to Tow Law and eastwards to the base of the limestone escarpment where the coal was still relatively close to the surface. As explained in Chapter One, the coal seams in Co. Durham dip down from West to East at an average angle of 5°. This meant that the further East the mines were located the deeper the coal seams were, and the greater the problems of flooding became, therefore making the mines more dependent on steam-powered water pumps. This also meant that the mines had to be able to produce larger quantities of coal in order to justify the cost of pumps and waggonways.

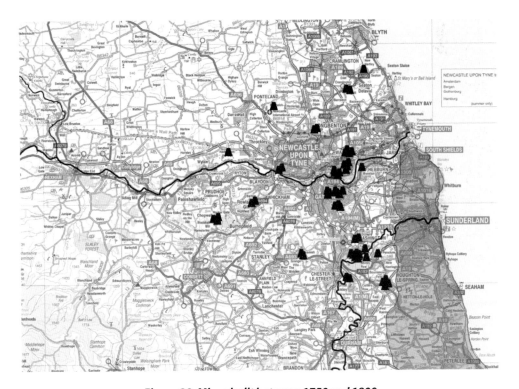

Figure 28: Mines built between 1750 and 1800

What was the driving force for the rapid development of the coalfield during this period of rapid expansion? The answer is quite simply the industrial revolution. This could with some degree of confidence be tied to a tiny village in Shropshire on the banks of the River Severn called Coalbrookdale (figure 29), where the first industrial blast furnace was built. But before we look at the effects of that let us continue to explore the other important developments which affected the coalfield.

Figure 29: A set of large blast furnaces at Blists Hill Open Air Museum, Ironbridge, Shropshire

Steam-driven Pumps

As the shallow coal continued to run out, mines had to be dug deeper and deeper. This meant going down below the water table with the resulting problem of flooding. Flooding became such a problem that a number of pits had to close. To be able to keep the mines dry they had to be drained but, unless they occurred above a river into which a drain adit could be dug this was a problem.

The tin mines in Cornwall had had similar problems for some time and Thomas Newcomen (born in Dartmouth, Devon in 1663) and James Watt (born in 1736 in Greenock, Scotland) developed low-pressure steam-driven pumps which could be used to drain them. Although Watt is usually credited with being the inventor of the steam engine Newcomen, who was a blacksmith, invented the first successful steam engine in 1712, over 20 years before Watt was born, to drain water from a coal mine in Staffordshire. In fact the first working steam engine was patented in 1698! The oldest existing Newcomen engine, built in 1791, which is claimed to be almost in its original form, can be found in the Science Museum in London (figure 30) and another example is preserved in the Royal Museum of Scotland in Edinburgh (figure 31).

Figure 30: (Above) 1791 Newcomen engine, Science Museum, London

Figure 31: (Right) Newcomen engine, Royal Museum of Scotland, Edinburgh

Watt went on to develop his engines even further with Matthew Boulton from Birmingham, and founded one of the most important engineering companies in the country at the time. The second engine that they constructed at Boulton's Soho works in Birmingham is preserved in the Science Museum in London. This in particular was fairly unreliable, as were many early engines, and gained the nickname 'Beelzebub'. At a later date it was modified and worked until 1848 pumping water at the site. Its nickname also changed to the much kinder 'Old Bess' by which it is now known (figure 32).

Figure 32: 'Old Bess', the second Boulton and Watt engine which is now preserved in the Science Museum in London

The first Newcomen steam engine used for draining a mine in this area is thought have been built on Washington Fell in 1714 for a colliery beside the River Wear. The next engine was installed at Norwood, near Ravensworth Castle, and these were followed by others at Oxclose and Byker. Prior to that, collieries on higher ground such as the ones at Whickham that could mine down lower seams without the fear of flooding had a distinct advantage over the mines in the valleys. This continued even after the first horse-powered water pumps were introduced in the Tyneside area from about 1580. The introduction of steam-driven Newcomen engines allowed a number of previously flooded pits to be re-opened.

Another important development that occurred at about the same time was the use of gun powder. This was used for blasting in the deeper mines. The combination of blasting and pumping allowed the deeper mines such as the 600 feet (183m) deep one at Walker to be dug in 1758. Other deep mines included Willington Pit (1775), Wallsend (1780s), Bigg's Main (1784) and Percy Main in 1796. It also allowed the Delavels to blast a new sea lane at Seaton Sluice (figure 33) which enabled them to increase the amount of coal they could export through the harbour. At the time this was the largest man-made excavation in the world.

Figure 33: The cut at Seaton Sluice

Chapter 4

The First Steam Locomotives

Richard Trevithick, was born in 1771 in Cornwall, took the Newcomen and Watt design and developed a high-pressure pump which was more efficient, smaller and therefore portable. He tested his design for a steam-powered road carriage, known as the 'puffing devil' or 'Captain Dick's puffer' at Camborne in Cornwall on Christmas Eve, 1801. Four days later, following another run, it caught fire whilst he was in a pub! He built a second steam carriage which ran several times in London. In fact the first steam wagon was built by a Frenchman named Nicholas Cugnot in 1769.

Figure 34: 'Gateshead engine' replica at Blists Hill Open Air Museum, Ironbridge, Shropshire

In 1802 the Dale Company in Coalbrookdale (the home of the industrial revolution) developed the first steam locomotive. Apart from being a Trevithick design, very little else is known about it other than it appears to have been similar to, but three-quarters of the size of, the engine constructed for the Pen-y-Darren Iron Works (see below) and that it took four months to build and used locally produced iron. It is thought to have had an accident but the subsequent inquiry was covered up and it was then converted into a stationary engine. Coalbrookdale, or Ironbridge as it is better known, was probably also the first place in the country to use iron rails. A replica of the locomotive, based on the 'Gateshead Engine' (figure 34) used to operate at Blists Hill Open Air Museum at Ironbridge but there appears to be some doubt about whether the original engine was actually built!

In the same year, the 'Grand Allies' developed the pit at Killingworth which became famous in the story of the early railways. Other deeper pits such as Burradon and Backworth were also dug north of the ninety Fathom Fault (164.5m displacement), a regionally important fault line which separates the generally shallower pits to the south of it from the deeper pits to the north.

The Pen-y-Darren

A second engine was built based on a Trevithick design in 1804 for the Pen-y-Darren Iron Works in Merthyr Tydfil. (This is also known as the 'Gateshead Engine', but see below.)

The Napoleonic wars led to an increase in the demand for iron ore, which required a more efficient method of transport from the four large iron works of Dowlais, Pen-y-Darren, Plymouth and Cyfarthfa, situated around Merthyr Tydfil.

Until then the iron ore had been carried on pack horses from Merthyr to the ports at Cardiff and Newport. To meet this demand the Glamorganshire Canal, which was completed by 1799, was constructed between Cardiff and Merthyr. Over its length of approximately 25 miles (40.2km) its descent of 510 feet (155.5m) required the construction of fifty locks. The canal posed two problems for some of the iron works owners; its largest share owner was Richard Crawshay, owner of the Cyfarthfa works.

The owners of the Pen-y-Darren and Dowlais iron works felt that the route of the canal favoured Plymouth and Cyfarthfa iron works and that the charges set by the canal company were unfair so they decided to provide their own means of transport. They chose a horse-drawn tram road, which was to be built from the iron works to Abercynon where it could meet up with the canal. However, only part of the tramway was completed, including the Plymouth Works Tunnel. This was also known as Trevithick's Tunnel, and it later became the first railway tunnel to be used by a locomotive.

Samuel Homfray, the owner of the Pen-y-Darren Iron Works, which opened in 1784, boasted that he could run a steam engine on the tramway which would be far more efficient than the canal barges, and a bet of 1000 guineas (500 guineas in some sources) was made with Richard Crawshay. The steam locomotive, known locally as the Puffing Devil, was designed to be able to pull wagons carrying 10 tons (10.6 tonnes) of iron along the nine mile (14.5km) long railway from the iron works to Abercynon. On 14 February (some sources put this as the 21st) 1804 this became the first operational steam locomotive-powered railway in the world. The steam engine travelling at a speed of 5 miles an hour (8kph), pulling 5 wagons holding 10 tons (10.6 tonnes) of iron ore and 70 men from the iron works to Abercynon. These 70 people therefore became the first people to travel on a locomotive-pulled train!

On the way, the chimney of the locomotive hit a low bridge which demolished both the chimney and bridge. Under the conditions of the bet, Trevithick had to undertake the repairs to the engine without any help. After repairs had been made it continued its journey and successfully reached the canal. Unfortunately, because of the steepness of the incline and the tight corners on the track, the engine did not have the power to pull the empty wagons back up the steep incline on the return trip.

On a later trip the engine carried 25 tons (25.4 tonnes) of iron. It only actually made three trips in total because like many of the later engines it kept breaking the rails due to its weight (5 tons (5.08tonnes)). During its third trip it broke a large number of rails and had to be towed back to Pen-y-Daren by horses - it was never used as a locomotive after that! Homfray decided that it would probably not reduce his transport costs so he abandoned the entire project.

A third Trevithick-designed locomotive was built by John Whinfield (Trevithick's agent in the North East), with some of the design work being carried out by John Steel from Pontop. This was tested at Pipewellgate in 1805. It had a horizontal drive and a large flywheel (as did most of the other designs at the time) and was based on the Pen-y-Darren engine design.

Figure 35: The 1806 Trevithick engine in the Science Museum, London

One of the reasons behind interest in the development of steam locomotives from the mine owners' in the North East was the continuous rise in the cost of horses that were needed to pull the coal waggons and of their food during the Napoleonic wars, when the demand for coal increased. These costs reduced profitability and, although the initial cost of laying iron rails and purchasing locomotives was high, the running costs were significantly lower. A similar Trevithick-designed engine, built around 1806 by Hazledine and Co. of Bridgnorth, Shropshire, is preserved in the Science Museum in London (figure 35).

At about the same time Christopher Blackett of Wylam Colliery also asked Trevithick to build him an engine, but he would not do it! Following his steam carriage Trevithick was persuaded by Davis Giddy, a wealthy Cornish landowner, to build another smaller steam engine which could run on a circular track. Calling it 'catch me if you can' he took this to Euston in North London, where it was used to give rides to the public between the 8 July and 18 September 1808. Unfortunately it didn't make enough money at two shillings (10p) a ticket, so he gave up. He then built another one which he tested in North London, but this one was difficult to control so he then gave making any more locomotives. It is interesting to speculate about how steam locomotives may have developed had these been successful.

In fact the first regular passenger-carrying railway in the world was the 5 miles (8km) line constructed between Swansea and Mumbles in the autumn of 1804. This was owned by the Oystermouth Railway or Tram Road Company and was primarily designed to carry coal from the coal mines at Blackpill and the limestone and ironstone from the mines along the route. The first horse-drawn passenger train was operated on 2 February 1807 by Benjamin French, who paid the railway company £20 per year to run his service. The owners of the line had close links to Samuel Homfray, the owner of the Pen-y-Darren Iron Works who, as we have seen, operated the first successful steam locomotive.

The Middleton Railway

In 1697 Ralph Brandling, a member of a coal-owning family based in Felling married Anne Leigh a member of mine owning family from Middleton, Leeds who inherited the Middleton Estate in 1706.

In 1717 Brandling introduced various mining innovations to Middleton from his Felling collieries to improve coal production and transportation. Ralph died in 1749 and was succeeded by his nephew who was also named Ralph a few weeks later. The next in line was sixteen year old Charles who following a period abroad returned home to Felling and Gosforth in 1751. Charles employed Richard Humble, a fellow tynesider, to take charge of his coal mining activities in Middleton. At the time there were three companies supplying coal in the Leeds area; the Brandlings of Middleton, the Wilkes of Beeston and the Fentons of Rothwell. To increase his productivity

Charles decided to build a waggonway, which opened on 26 September 1758. The success of the waggonway led to a significant increase in coal production and the construction of a number of smaller branch lines. The waggonway system continued to expand using men and experience imported from Tyneside until local workers could be trained to do the same work.

Charles died at Gosforth in 1802 and was succeeded by his son Charles John Brandling who built even more waggonways even though the coal trade had been hit by a major recession since 1800. In 1807 Charles John brought in Thomas Fenwick and John Watson both from Newcastle to undertake a detailed evaluation of his coal assets. The same year he employed John Blenkinsop (born in Low Heworth in 1783) as his viewer (manager) at his Felling Colliery.

Blenkinsop also undertook a review of the Middleton Colliery in 1808 which led to the construction of a new waggonway. He patented (patent number 3431) a locomotive which worked on cogged wheels on the 10 April 1811. The patent only covered the cog wheel and track system. The locomotive was designed by Matthew Murray (born in Newcastle in 1765). Murray joined by David Wood built a foundry to be able to build locomotives and rails. They were then joined by James Fenton and John Marshall who together founded the company Fenton, Murray & Wood which extended the original foundry.

On the 24 June 1812 Blenkinsop and Murray tested their first locomotive. It managed to pull eight coal waggons each carrying 3 tons (3.048 tonnes) a distance of 1.5 miles (2.4km). The foundry built six or seven engines which effectively became the first 'class' (locomotives built to the same basic design) of locomotive to be built. The first locomotive was named Salamanca. Middleton became the first regular profitable use of steam locomotives on any railway in the world (figure 36).

Figure 36: Three views of the Middleton Railway; (left) the preserved line, (centre) the 'blue plaque' celebrating its place in history and (right) Moor Road which follows part of the line of the rack system

Blenkinsop then built three more locomotives, the Prince Regent in 1812, the Lord Wellington in 1813 and the Marquis Wellington in 1814. Each locomotive weighed approximately five tons (5.08 tonnes) and could pull twenty times their own weight. The four of them together replaced the 50 horses and 200 men that had previously been used pull the coal waggons. The Salamanca cost £380 including £30 payable to

W. West the local agent and Trevithick holder. James Hewitt was employed as the world's first professional engine driver. In February 1813 a 13 year old boy named John Bruce was killed by one of the trains and therefore became the first member of the public to be killed by a train. On the 28 February 1818 the Salamanca's boiler exploded killing its engineer.

A month after arriving at Middleton the Willington (actually the third engine to be built) was sold to the Kenton and Coxlodge Colliery on Tyneside where it operated on the Biggs Main Wooden Waggonway which ran from West Gosforth to Heaton and Wallsend. Two other, larger locomotives were then ordered for the colliery and the mine owners converted 2 miles (3.2km) of the waggonway to the rack system needed for these engines. This ran from the Jubilee Pit to the Ouseburn Bridge at Haddricks Mill (which is now the route of the Jubilee Road).

When this opened in 1813 it was the first real steam locomotive powered railway in the North East and each locomotive was able to pull 16 coal waggons at a time. Robert Dalglish of the Orrell Colliery in Wigan was so impressed by the locos and track system that he order three engines, two to work on the waggonway and one as a spare. These were unofficially named the 'Yorkshire Horse' and the Walking Horse'. The first Middleton engine was sometimes known as the 'Stalking Horse'.

The Steam Elephant

William Chapman, who was born in Whitby in 1749, patented a different system which used a heavy chain laid down the centre of the tracks. This wound around a drum on the locomotive which used it to pull the engine along the track. The first locomotive using this design was built in Derby in 1813 and was tested at Heaton Colliery between 1814 and 1815 before the mine flooded and was closed down.

Chapman also invented the 'bogie' which is a series of axels held on a moveable frame which allowed locomotives (and later coaches) to go around corners more easily. He used this on a locomotive at Heaton in 1813. He built a second engine, known as the Heaton II, which had eight wheels on two bogies at Ouseburn near Heaton in 1814 which was used at the Lambton Collieries.

His third engine was built in 1815 for John Buddle, the manager of the Wallsend Colliery by Hawks & Co. at Gateshead. Buddle was also the viewer and chief engineer at the Heaton and Lampton collieries. This engine, which had six wheels and was known as the 'Steam Elephant' did not work very well on the wooden rails at Wallsend so in 1816 it was moved to Washington Colliery which also had wooden rails. It was then moved back to Wallsend once they had laid iron rails and eventually ended up at the Hetton Colliery. A working replica of this engine operates at the Beamish Open Air Museum (figure 37).

Figure 37: A working replica of the Steam Elephant at Beamish Open Air Museum

One of the problems with the original cast iron rails is that the weight of the early steam locomotives meant that they kept breaking the rails because cast iron is relatively brittle. To prevent this many engines were rebuilt with more wheels to spread the load. When wrought iron rails were introduced, which were stronger, many of the locomotives were rebuilt again with fewer wheels which made them easier to operate and maintain.

The Wylam Engines

Wylam Colliery was the site where many of the most important people involved in the development of the steam locomotive lived or worked (figure 38 shows one of the signs at the entrance to the village designed to celebrate its historic past).

Figure 38: The sign at the entrance to Wylam village

In 1808 the wooden tracks of the waggonway were replaced with 'plate' rails (remember that these have flanges on them). In 1812 William Hedley of Wylam Colliery together with Timothy Hackworth (figure 39) and Christopher Blackett carried out a series of experiments to see how good steam locomotives would be when working on iron rails. The tack was probably laid between Wylam Cottage and the back of Wylam Hall. It was thought that they would slip too much and would therefore be unable to pull enough coal trucks to make them worth using, hence the use of cogged wheels by Blenkinsop and Murray (see Middleton Railway). Their first engine, built by Thomas Walters, was based on the Trevithick Pen-y-Darren engine, but was designed to be lighter to avoid the problems of breaking the rails. This engine was built at the Whinfield Foundry in Pipewellgate, Gateshead and was known as the 'Gateshead Engine'. It was used for trials at the iron works but Blackett did not accept the engine for use at the colliery so it was converted in to an air blower for the foundry! This may have been because he thought that it may have damaged the wooden rails. Following this they conducted a second series of experiments at Wylam using a 'man powered' waggon to see whether smooth wheels on a smooth track would provide enough grip to do away with the extra expense of using cogs or chains.

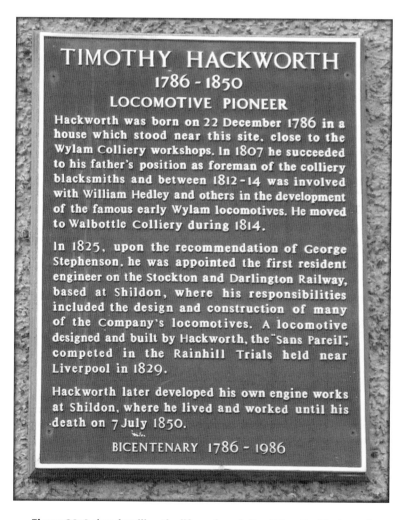

Figure 39: A sign detailing the life and exploits of Timothy Hackworth

In 1813 they had three other engines built to a more advanced design, Puffing Billy (which worked for 50 years and is now in the Science Museum (figure 40)), Wylam Dilly (preserved in the Royal Museum of Scotland in Edinburgh (figure 41)) and Lady Mary (which was scrapped in the 1820s).

Figure 40: Puffing Billy in the Science Museum, London

Figure 41: Wylam Dilly in the Royal Museum of Scotland, Edinburgh

All of these engines ran on plate tracks which were only used at Wylam until they replaced the wheels and re-laid the track with stronger edge rails. It is interesting to note that when Puffing Billy was built there were only about 25 miles (40km) of steam locomotive tracks in the country but when it retired there were tens of thousands! There is also a working replica of Puffing Billy at the Beamish Open Air Museum (figure 42).

Figure 42: Puffing Billy replica, Beamish Open Air Museum

By the summer of 1815 although locomotives were in use at Kenton and Coxbridge, Heaton, Lambton, Newbottle, Wallsend, Wylam and Killingworth, only the ones at Wylam were really successful. Locomotives did not come in to general use until the 1830s. Until then Wylam was the only completely steam locomotive powered railway in the country.

In 1822 during the Keelmen's strike, Hedley converted Wylam Dilly to drive a set of paddles and mounted it on a keelboat so that it could tow coal barges on the Tyne. Once the strike had ended he converted it back and it continued to work on the waggonway.

George Stephenson, known locally as 'Wylam Geordie', was born in a cottage at Wylam in 1781 (figure 43 to 45). In fact the Wylam Waggonway ran past his front door!

Figure 43: The cottage where George Stephenson was born, next to the Wylam Waggonway

Figure 44: Part of the route of the waggonway at Wylam

Figure 45: The sign (left) on the cottage commemorating George Stephenson and the National Trust entrance sign (right) at the entrance

Between 1813 and 1815 the development of steam locomotives moved from Wylam to Killingworth, to where Stephenson and Nicholas Wood, who were both from Wylam, had moved. Whilst working at Killingworth Colliery he conducted his own experiments with steam engines and built his first locomotive, called My Lord, in 1814 and a second one in 1815 named Blucher, although it has been suggested that My Lord may have been renamed as Blucher and therefore could be the same engine. Stephenson lived in Dial Cottage, which is now owned by the National Trust (figure 46), close to the Killingworth Waggonway; it was here that his son Robert was born. Together they were later to play an incredibly important part in developing the railways as we know them today. George Stephenson also developed a safety lamp at the same time as, but independently of, Sir Humphrey Davy. Davy's lamp was first tested on the 1 January 1816 at Hebburn Colliery.

Figure 46: Dial Cottage, Killingworth. The small photograph shows the sun dial which George and his son Robert made. It is dated 11 August, 1816

The next important stage in the story of the development of mining and the railways switches from north of the Tyne to south of the Wear.

By 1793 there were ten coal staithes in the Fatfield area, the highest navigable point on the River Wear, which were connected to thirty pits in the local area (figure 48). As we have seen, the coal was then loaded on to small boats which carried it to Sunderland, where it was then loaded on to larger, sea-going ships for export. This process and the charges imposed by the keelmen added a significant cost to coal production, which reduced the profitability of the pits, so a number of mine owners looked for ways of bypassing this system. Fatfield is also on the tidal part of the river (figure 47), which meant that the keel boats could not necessarily operate throughout the day. A map which shows the locations of all the pits and waggonways in the immediate area around Fatfield has been included to show the intensity of early coal mining, although it should be pointed out that not all of the pits were operational at the same time.

Figure 47: Two views of the River Wear at Fatfield show the difference in the height of the river at high tides (left) and low tide (right)

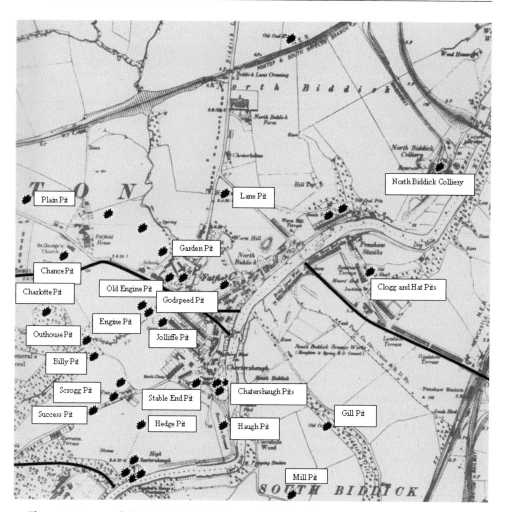

Figure 48: A map of pits in Fatfield, Washington. The black lines represent the waggonways which were used to transport coal to the staithes located on either side of the river

Chapter 5

The Railways and Mining Come of Age

The Hetton Lyons Colliery

The Hetton Lyons Pit, owned by Arthur Mowbray, an unsuccessful businessman, was the first one to be dug successfully through the Magnesian Limestone to find coal. The first attempt had been at Rainton Bridge but this encountered problems. It may seem odd now, but until then everyone assumed that the Coal Measures ended at the edge of the limestone escarpment. It was William Smith, a canal designer and the 'father of modern geology' who persuaded Mowbray and his partners John Lyons, Colonel Braddyll (a local land owner), and Archibald Cochrane (who formed the Hetton Colliery Company) to dig a shaft through the limestone to find the coal. Due to the cost involved in undertaking such an enterprise, no single mine owner could afford to sink a shaft that deep, so this was the first time a company was specifically established for such a project. There are some reports that, following problems at Hetton, work stopped and in 1811 and, on Smith's advice, Braddyll started a pit at Haswell. Here the limestone was relatively thin, but the underlying Yellow Sands were quite thick. They encountered major problems with flooding when they reached the sands, and abandoned the site. They then started the Janet Shaft at Hetton Lyons on the 19December 1820 but encountered similar major problems with flooding when they reached the underlying Permian Yellow Sands. This time, however, they completed it and the Blossom Pit reaching the Hutton Coal seam in January 1823 at a depth of 882 feet (269m) and a cost of £1,300 (figure 49 and 50). This then became the first deep coal mine to go through the

Permian limestones and led to the opening up of the most important part of the Durham Coalfield. They did not attempt to dig another shaft at Haswell until 1831. The pit at Haswell was eventually developed on a different site and remained open until 1896.

Figure 49: This car park is on the site of the first deep shaft, the Janet Shaft, at Hetton Lyons Colliery

Figure 50: Mine building at the Hetton Lyons Colliery

To increase profitability the company decided to bypass the waggonways to Fatfield and the inherent cost of transportation along the Wear. They opted to build their own railway from Hetton Lyons directly to Sunderland and they commissioned George Stephenson and his brother Robert as resident engineer (figure 51), to design and build the eight-mile (12.8km) railway line from the colliery at Hetton Lyons to the staithes at Sunderland.

Figure 51: Robert Stephenson's house opposite Hetton Lyons Colliery

The mine engineer was Nicholas Wood, a name closely associated with the Stephenson's (figure 52). Due to the nature of the landscape the Stephenson's included a series of stationary steam engines, pulling ropeways, self-acting inclined planes, and steam locomotives. This was based on the shorter line that had been designed by George Stephenson for the Killingworth Colliery, and construction of the Hetton Railway began in March 1821.

Figure 52: Nicholas Wood's house in Hetton-le Hole

The first locomotive used at Hetton, which actually worked at Wallsend before moving there, was designed by Chapman and Buddle. It probably worked at Hetton for about 10 years. Although it was named Fox, it was more generally known as the 'Steam Elephant', which was actually more of a generic term used for a number of engines working at Wallsend and Hetton at the time, rather than a name attached to a particular locomotive. A painting exists which shows the 'Steam Elephant' at Hetton, but it is interesting to note that it is not on the railway tracks. The Hetton line was built using 'edge' tracks and, as noted above, the 'Steam Elephant' was designed for use on 'plate' rails. This gave the locomotive the advantage that without the flanged wheels it could operate like a free-moving steam engine.

At this time Stephenson and Wood had been working on a number of changes in locomotive design at Killingworth, which were incorporated in to a new 'Killingworth Travelling Engine design'. This was used as the basis for three locos, named Dart, Tallyho and Star (after local race horses), which were built by Stephenson and his son Robert in their new Newcastle works. Each locomotive could pull seventeen loaded coal waggons at an average speed of 4mph (6.4kph). Stephenson actually sold five locomotives to the railway but these were fairly unreliable and were eventually replaced in the 1830s by other engines.

Killingworth Billy (figure 53), which is preserved at the Stephenson Railway Museum in North Shields, is one of only five pre-Rocket engines that still exist (the others are Puffing Billy, Wylam Dilly, Locomotion and the Hetton engine). This was built in 1826 and, although it was a further development of Stephenson's Killingworth Travelling Engine design it was to a large extent the same as the Wylam engines. The improvements made by Stephenson, William Losh of the Walker Iron Works in Newcastle and Nicholas Wood resulted in Killingworth Billy becoming the first commercially-successful steam locomotive. It continued to work until 1881 pulling coal waggons from Killingworth to the top of the incline plane at Wallsend. Stephenson and Losh not only jointly patented the engine design but they also patented their own design for cast-iron tracks.

Figure 53: Killingworth Billy, preserved at the Stephenson Railway Museum, North Shields

When the Hetton line opened on 18 November 1822 it was the first railway in the world that was specifically designed to be mechanically powered over its entire length (figure 54).

Figure 54: One of the commemorative signs at Hetton

However, steam locomotives were only used on two short, flat sections of the line - a section in the middle and one near the pit. Using this route it only took two hours to transport the coal from the pit to the staithes, which made a significant saving in time as well as cost. Eventually the locos were taken off the middle section and only used in the area around the pit. The rest of the railway used inclined planes to pull the waggons over steeper sections such as the slope at Copt Hill (figure 55).

Figure 55: Two photographs of the Hetton line at Copt Hill

When the line opened for the first time a huge crowd came to watch because, at the time, it was regarded as one of the engineering wonders of the world. One of the early Hetton engines, which may have been modified in the 1860s is preserved at Shildon (figure 56) and until recently was on show at the Open Air Museum at Beamish.

Figure 56: The Hetton engine preserved at the National Railway Museum, Shildon

These were not the only revolutions involved with the development of the Hetton Lyons Colliery. The Janet shaft was also the first to use the 'tubbing' method of shaft construction where the shaft was encased in metal segments to stop flooding. The opening of the mine had a big impact on Hetton - in 1801 the population was only 212 but by 1821 this had grown to 919.

Two other pits, Elemore and Eppleton, were opened in the immediate area and were connected to the railway (figure 57). By 1826 the three pits were' producing 318,000 tons (323,088 tonnes) of coal, which was worth about £174,000. At the time this was the largest mining combine in England. Eventually a branch line was also added to the pit at Silksworth. The line continued to be used until the 1950s when Hetton Lyons closed and Eppleton and Elemore then sent their coal underground via Murton and by rail to either Sunderland or Seaham. The Hetton Colliery Railway actually closed on Wednesday 9 September 1959 and they started dismantling the line the following day! The last section was finally removed on 20 November 1960 which means that nothing of this historic feat of engineering has been preserved.

Figure 57: The route of the waggonway from Eppleton to the Hetton Railway

In 1822 Lord Lambton bought the Newbottle Colliery, which had a waggonway that allowed him to transport coal directly to Sunderland without having to pay the additional costs of transport along the River Wear. He then added his other pits at Cocken, Littletown and Sherburn to the system.

Also in 1822 William Hutton, Benjamin Hick and Peter Rothwell, all major cloth manufacturers in the midlands, formed the Bolton and Leigh Railway Company and asked George Stephenson to build a railway which would give then an alternative method of transport to the canal system. At the time the canal owners effectively had a monopoly on transporting cloth, and with the increase in production there was a worry that the canal system would not be able to meet the demand. The 7.5 mile (12km) railway opened on 1 August 1828 with a Stephenson-built locomotive named Lancashire Witch. Some sections of the railway were too steep for locos to operate and so cable haul systems were used to transport the wagons. The first passengers were carried on 13 June 1831 and the line was eventually linked to the Liverpool and Manchester Railway.

The 'Rainton Royalty' and Seaham

Figure 58 shows the mines that opened between 1800 and 1850, indicating a significant increase in the number of new mines. Prior to 1822 the majority of the new mines were dug in the Washington/Chester-le-Street area and north of the Tyne. Once coal had been proved to exist beneath the limestone, the large mines which really began the 'golden period' of the Durham Coalfield opened.

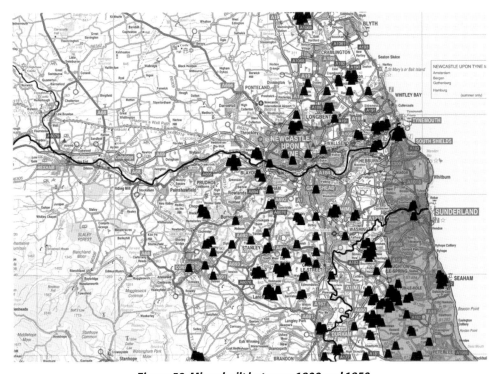

Figure 58: Mines built between 1800 and 1850

Although the 'Rainton Royalty' was owned by the Dean and Chapter of Durham Cathedral, it was leased by Lord Londonderry who developed the pits around Rainton. The Rainton Colliery was a collection of pits, some of which had been producing coal since at least the 1650s. There were six large pits, Nicholson's, Rainton Meadows, Plain, Woodside, Hunters House (or Hutton House) and Resolution and a number of smaller pits including Quarry Pit, Annabella, North Pit, The Knott, Old Engine and Pontop Pit. Coal from the pits was transported to the Staithes at Penshaw via Colliery Row, Junction Row and Shiney Row in horse drawn waggons.

Lord Londonderry (Sir Henry Vane-Tempest) and his daughter Frances Anne Emily Vane-Tempest, who inherited the pits after he died in 1813 (when she was only 13), also developed their own waggonway to take coal to the projected new harbour at Seaham. This would take away the need and cost of transporting the coal to the Penshaw/Fatfield area and then down the Wear to Sunderland, which would save around £10,000 a year.

This waggonway crossed under but had no junction with the Hetton line at Copt Hill, and remained in operation until 1896 when the Rainton pits closed. Following this closure a junction was constructed which then allowed coal from Hetton, Elemore and Eppleton to be transported to Seaham if there were problems at Sunderland. By 1818 the Rainton Collieries were producing an operational profit of around £60,000 a year!

When Frances Anne Emily's grandparents, Sir Henry Vane and Frances Tempest had married they brought together two famous families that were members of the Grand Alliance (Sir George Vane and Sir Nicholas Tempest).

In 1819 Frances Anne Emily married Charles Stewart, who then bought the estates of Seaham and Dalden on 13 October 1821 for £63,000. Whilst trying to raise the money to build the harbour at Dalden Ness (which was renamed as Seaham in 1843), he developed four other mines, the Adventure Pit (in 1822) the Alexandrina or Letch Pit (in 1824), and Dun Well and Hazard pits (both in 1825) at Rainton. Between 1826 and 1828 he also developed a new colliery complex at Pittington which included the Londonderry, Adolphus and Buddle pits, the latter named after his mine manager. He sub-leased the Dun Well, Hazard pits and North Pit to William Russell of Brancepeth. This included permission to transport coal to the staithes at Penshaw.

The Port at Seaham (figure 59) which was designed by Thomas Telford and John Rennie with the original dock planned by William Chapman was finally built in 1828 and the first coals were transported along the line from Rainton on the 25 July 1831. Originally the line was only five miles (8km) long but this gradually increased to 18 miles (29km) as a network of branch lines to new pits were added. This included the South Hetton Pit which was built by Colonel Braddyll in 1833, Belmont Pit (1835), North Hetton Colliery (1838), Antrim Pit (1842), Ernest Pit (1849) near Durham, and a ninth pit at Rainton named Lady Seaham.

Figure 59: North dock at Seaham harbour

In 1844 High Pit at Seaton Colliery was constructed by the North Hetton and Grange Coal Company next to the Rainton and Seaham Railway, on land leased from Lord Londonderry. The first main coal seam was reached in 1849, and production began in 1852. Lord Londonderry developed his Low Pit at Seaham Colliery in 1849 on land adjacent to the Seaton Colliery. In fact, the shafts were only 150 yards (137m) apart! Seaham Colliery was the first mine to work out under the sea floor. Following the mining disaster at Hartley Colliery in 1862 when part of the head gear fell down the only shaft to the mine, trapping and causing the deaths of 204 miners, there was a change in the law which meant that every colliery had to have two shafts, so that miners had another means of escape and that air circulation could be improved (see New Hartley Colliery accident below). The North Hetton and Grange Coal Company sold High Pit to Lord Londonderry in 1864 and the two collieries were joined together as Seaham Colliery. The first coal produced from Low Pit reached the surface on the 27 March 1852.

The discovery of coal under the Magnesian Limestone led to the construction of a series of large collieries along the coast which could work coal out under the sea. Digging the shafts through the thick sequence of limestones and dolomites was difficult enough but the miners encountered real problems when they had to dig through the underlying Yellow Sands. These are generally very soft, friable sands which hold huge amounts of water. The following is a contemporary description of the problems encountered whilst constructing the shafts at Murton in 1838:

> The winning of this colliery was one of the most difficult and expensive undertakings of the kind on record. The sinking of the first shaft was commenced on 19 February 1838, and a second shaft was begun two months later. Each shaft was 14 feet (4.26m) diameter, and both were carried on simultaneously. Little water was met with until a depth of 32 fathoms (58.5m) was reached, when the sand-feeders were encountered, which were successively tubbed on, thus freeing the shafts from water. On 26 June 1839, however, the sand feeders burst through the bottom of the shaft, throwing up with tremendous force four feet (1.2m) of strong limestone which intervened between the bottom of the shaft and the sand. Such was the violence of the eruption that before the capstans could heave up the pumps, they were all chocked, and more than ten feet (3.05m) of sand deposited in the pit. Additional engine-power was then applied to both shafts, and for some time nearly 5000 gallons per minute (22,730lpm) were drawn to the bank, but without making any sensible effect. A third shaft was then commenced, and in six months reached a depth of 73 fathoms (133.5m), when two pumping-engines, made also to pump, were placed upon it. The total engine-power employed was 1478 horse-power in all, which required 34 boilers to maintain. The obstructions caused by the sand mixing with the water frequently wore out the buckets within two or three hours. It is stated that the leather buckets alone cost by the hour £11.5s (£11.25), that three tan yards had to supply the requisite quaintly

of leather, and that 100 tons (101.6 tonnes) of coal per day were needed
to feed the furnaces. At last, in spite of almost unparalleled difficulties,
water was drawn from the pit at the rate of 1000 gallons per minute
(4,546lpm), the whole the feeders were stopped back by metal tubbing,
and the shafts were at length completed through this formidable quicksand.
(Whellan's 1894 Directory of County Durham, reproduced from the Durham
Mining Museum web site.)

Monkwearmouth Colliery (which was originally known Pemberton Main and later
became Wearmouth Colliery) began construction in 1826, and took seven years to
reach the first major coal seam, the Bensham Seam, at a depth of 1,059 feet (323m).
This was 5 feet 8 inches (1.75m) thick and was producing between 40-50,000 tons
(40,640-50,800 tonnes) of coal a year by 1835. The Lower Hutton Seam, which
was 4 feet 8 inches (1.32m) thick was reached on 4 April 1846 at a depth of 1,722
feet (524.9m). At the time this was the deepest mine in the world.

Three other significant developments took place during this period which increased
the use of coal. In 1803 coal gas was used for the first time to provide lighting and in
1830 coke was introduced as a replacement for coal in blast furnaces. Coke was not a
new invention. It was first used in 1644 in Derbyshire for drying malt but it is
thought that coke was not produced in our area until 1763. Finally, the opening up
of iron mining in Cleveland led to a large expansion of the coal field. In 1854 the
Northumberland and Durham coalfields together produced nearly 15.5 million tons
(15.75 million tonnes) out of the total UK production of about 57 million tons
(57.9 million tonnes), and by 1891 production from the two coal fields had risen to
just over 39 million tons (39.6 million tonnes).

The Stockton and Darlington Railway

Mining also continued to develop southward towards and beyond Durham. As early
as 1767 there were plans to build a canal between Darlington and Stockton, and as
the coal field continued to develop James Brindley and Robert Whitworth were
asked to survey a possible route. They produced their results in 1769 but the funds
could not the raised to build it. In 1810 the idea was proposed again when the Tees
Navigation Company opened up their 'New Cut', which bypassed the Tees between
Stockton and the coast. By 1818 a number of merchants in the Stockton area were
again considering the idea of building a canal between Stockton and Darlington
which would connect Stockton to the South Durham coalfield. Merchants in Yarm
and Darlington were unhappy with the idea because it would bypass Yarm, which
historically was the main port on the Tees. The idea stalled until Edward Pease, a
retired wool merchant, raised the idea of building a railway instead. All of those who
were interested in investing in and supporting the venture met in the George &
Dragon in Yarm on 12 February 1820 (figure 60). The Act of Parliament which was
required to authorise the building of the railway was initially voted down, but Pease

tried again in 1821 and this time it was passed. George Overton then was asked to survey a route and George Stephenson was later asked to see whether he could improve on it.

Figure 60: The George & Dragon in Yarm

The 24-mile (38.4km) line started at Witton Park Colliery to the west of Bishop Auckland and ended at the coal staithes in the port at Stockton. The railway eventually led to the further opening up of the coalfield south west of Durham after 1825. Edward Pease commissioned George Stephenson to design and build the railway, which he thought would use horse-drawn waggons. But Stephenson argued that using a steam-driven locomotive would be cheaper and more reliable. He chose the width between the tracks (the gauge) to be 4 feet 8 ½ inches (1.43m), which was the same as the gauge on his Killingworth line. He arrived at this figure by averaging the gauges of all the waggonways he had visited in the north east. As 90 per cent of the railways then used this gauge it was established as the Standard Gauge by an Act of Parliament in 1846 and has subsequently became the standard gauge for railways world-wide.

Figure 61: 48 Bridge Road in Stockton where the first tracks were laid for the Stockton and Darlington Railway on 23 May 1822

Construction of the railway line began on 13 May 1822, and the first section of the track was laid on 23 May, almost six months before the Hetton line became operational. The first rails were laid down by Thomas Meynell, the Chairman of the company, at St John's Well, close to the River Tees. Today the site is marked by a metal plaque on the corner of Bridge Road where it joins the 1825 Way. In fact there are three different plaques on the site. One indicates that the first rails were laid at a level crossing adjacent to the building, the second commemorates the opening of the railway and the third indicates that 48 Bridge Road (figure 61) was the world's first railway ticket office.

Figure 61(a): Two commemorative plaques from 48 Bridge Road, Stockton

Stephenson and his son Robert used the 'Killingworth design' when building Locomotion 1 for the new Stockton and Darlington Railway (figures 62 and 63).

Figure 62: The original Locomotion preserved at the Darlington Railway Museum

Figure 63: A working replica of Locomotion at Beamish Open Air Museum

This railway, based on the Hetton Railway, was primarily designed to transport coal from the collieries around Bishop Auckland to the coal staithes in Stockton, which led to the establishment of Stockton as a port. On 27 September 1825, the day the railway officially opened, Locomotion, was driven by George Stephenson, with Timothy Hackworth as the guard. Having first collected coal from the Phoenix Pit, and flour, the train was pulled by horses and stationary engines until it reached the base (on the Shildon side) of the Brusselton Incline. It was here that Locomotion 1 was attached to the waggons - close to, but not necessarily outside, the New Mason's Arms where a sign indicates that this was the first railway station (figure 64).

Figure 64: The New Mason's Inn, which was the first railway station in Shildon

Locomotion 1 then pulled 30 waggons, which carried 600 people at an average speed of 12mph (19.2km). Three other locomotives followed, Hope in November 1825, Black Diamond in April 1826 and Diligence in May 1826. Reliability was one of the biggest problems with the early locomotives. Most of them spent a great deal of time in the engine sheds, under repair. The other major problem was their weight, which meant they kept breaking the rails. To help to prevent this Stephenson recommended that the railway use 15 foot (4.6m) wrought iron rails made by Michael Longridge's, Bedlington Iron Works rather than the 4 foot (1.2m) cast iron rails made in his own works. Even though wrought iron rails were used, the engines still used cast iron wheels which kept breaking due to the unevenness of the rails and their tendency to 'lift' during cold weather. The amount of damage caused by these problems was so great that it is thought that the railways had to replace as many as 1,500 wheels a month during cold weather!

Once the railway had settled down to its regular work pattern Locomotion was only actually used on a 2.5 mile (4km) section of the line and horses were used on the rest of the railway to pull all passenger trains. Locomotives were only used to transport coal waggons but this is said to have reduced the price of coal from something like 18 shillings (75p) per ton (77p per tonne) before they were used on the line to as little as 8s.6d (43p) per ton (44p per tonne). Steam locos were only used on the flatter sections from Shildon eastwards. The western end included steam-driven incline planes which pulled the coal waggons over the hills at Etherley and Brusselton (figure 65). Part of the engine house still exists at Brusselton (figure 66) together with a short section of the original square stone rail sleepers and the parapets of a bridge (figure 67) and footpath which follows part of the route (figure 68).

Figure 65: One of the inclines planes at Brusselton

Figure 66: The engine house at the top of the inclined plane at Brusselton

Figure 67 (left): A section of original stone sleepers from the Stockton and Darlington Railway preserved at Brusselton

Figure 68 (above): Part of the route of the Stockton and Darlington Railway through Shildon

Locomotion is now preserved in the Darlington Railway Museum (figure 62) and there is a working replica of it at the Beamish Open Air Museum (figure 63). A year after the Stockton and Darlington line opened the Stephenson's built the Killingworth Billy, which included a number of improvements.

Timothy Hackworth, who was born in Wylam and became a blacksmith at the pit before moving to Wallbottle Colliery, then moved to Shildon where he became the resident engineer. He built his first engine, Royal George, using parts of another engine, Chittaprat, which was larger and more advanced than Stephenson's Locomotion. This was considered to be one of the most advanced locomotives at that time. Soho Cottage, Hackworth's house at Shildon, is now open to the public together with the National Railway Museum complex at Shildon.

The Rainhill Trials

Manchester was the world's first large industrial town, and by the 1820s it had established itself as an important centre for the cotton industry, importing large quantities of cotton from America and exporting equally large volumes of cotton goods, via the docks at Liverpool. One of the problems the mill owners faced was that all transport to and from Liverpool was by canal, a journey which often took so long that the cotton rotted on the journey. They also objected to the effective monopoly that the Bridgewater Canal Company had on their transport needs and costs, so they decided to come up with their own transport route. The resulting Act of Parliament led to the founding of the Liverpool and Manchester Railway Company, whose directors wanted the railway to be powered completely by locomotives.

In order to find the best engines available the directors decided to run a competition which became known as the famous Rainhill Trials (figure 69). They appointed two consultants, James Walker and John Urpeth Rastrick, to oversee the process. Rastrick together with Foster built the Agenoria in 1829 for the Shutt End Colliery near Birmingham, which although it was a contemporary of the Rocket, was built to a much simpler design. This is preserved in the National Railway Museum in York (figure 70). They also appointed three judges to oversee the competition, John Urpeth Rastrick, Nicholas Wood (who when he was sixteen had worked at the same colliery as George Stephenson), and John Kennedy, a wealthy cotton processor from Manchester.

Figure 69: A commemorative sign on outskirts of Rainhill

Figure 70: The Agenoria preserved in the the National Railway Museum, York

The Stephenson's entered the Rocket (figure 71), a locomotive which included many of the improvements they had introduced on their previous engines. It was one of five locomotives that were entered for the trials, which were set up to see which locomotive was capable of reliably running over the 1.5 mile (2.4km) track twenty times, the equivalent to the journey between the two cities. Actually, the Rocket was really designed by Robert and his staff at Newcastle, rather than George Stephenson, who had been given the job of designing the route for the railway. The other four locos were the Novelty, built by Braithwaite and Ericsson, Sans Pareil built by Hackworth, Perseverance built by Burstall, and Cycloped which was actually powered by two horses walking on a treadmill rather than by a steam engine and was therefore not allowed to take part in the competition! Perseverance was damaged whilst it was being transported from Liverpool and was not repaired in time to take part in the trials. Novelty performed really well but then broke down; Sans Pareil performed well but had continuous problems and did not finish the trials. Only the Rocket kept going to the end and therefore won the competition. It achieved a top speed of 29 mph (46kph) and travelled a distance of 70 miles (112km) (equivalent to the return journey between Manchester and Liverpool) without breaking down. This was a major event in the area and it is estimated that between ten and fifteen thousand people turned up to see the competition.

Figure 71: The original Rocket, preserved in the Science Museum, London

George Stephenson was asked to survey and supervise the construction of the line between Manchester and Liverpool. This included the construction of a large tunnel at Edgehill, a cutting two miles long (3.2km), and 70 feet (21.3m) deep at Olive Mount, a viaduct across the Sankey Valley, and tracks across a 12-mile (19.2km) section of marshland at Chat Moss outside Manchester. To overcome the latter Stephenson designed a track-bed laid on mats of heather and brushwood. The iron tracks for the railway were made at the Pen-y-Darren Iron Works where, as we have seen, the first successful steam engine had operated. The Pen-y-Darren works also made the cables for the Menai Bridge.

The railway was officially opened on 14 July 1830 with eight locomotives: the Rocket, Meteor, Comet, Dart, Arrow, Phoenix, North Star and Northumbrian. Rocket was driven by Joseph Locke, Phoenix was driven by Robert Stephenson, North Star driven by George's brother Robert, and the Northumbrian was driven by George Stephenson. The Northumbrian, which incorporated all the best features of the others, was the fastest and the most powerful of the eight engines. They all left Liverpool station with various carriages, the Northumbrian drawing the Duke of Wellington and other dignitaries including the MP for Liverpool, William Huskisson, President of the Board of Trade. During one of the stops Huskisson got out of the train and was either hit by or fell under the Rocket. He died later that day from his injuries and thus became the first person to be killed by a steam locomotive. During the run back to Liverpool with the dying Huskisson the Northumbrian achieved speeds of up to 40mph (64kph).

In fact the claim that this was the first railway death is not strictly true as there had been a number of previous deaths associated with explosions caused by the build-up of high pressures due to engine drivers tying down the steam safety release valves. These included two such incidents on the Stockton and Darlington Railway. The first in March 1828 killed John Gillipee, a novice fireman on his first run on the Diligence which was being driven by James Stephenson, the eldest brother of George. The second involved the Locomotion, which killed its driver in July of the same year. The Salamanca had blown up for the same reason back in 1818! Twelve spectators were also killed at Newbottle Colliery in 1818 when the boiler of an early locomotive blew up.

Figure 72: A replica of the Rocket in the National Railway Museum, York

The Rocket is preserved in the Science Museum in London (figure 70) and there is a sectioned replica (figure 72), at the National Railway Museum in York. The Sans Pareil (which means 'without equal'), which was built by Timothy Hackworth in 1829, is preserved at the National Railway Museum at Shildon (figure 73), close to the site of the engine shed in which it was built. The museum also has a working replica (figure 74).

Figure 73: The original Sans Pareil preserved at the National Railway Museum, Shildon

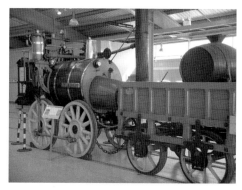

Figure 74: A working replica of the Sans Pareil at the National Railway Museum, Shildon

The rest as they say is history! Within a month of the opening of the Liverpool and Manchester Railway, fourteen stagecoach services closed down and within five years it was carrying 500,000 passengers and 350,000 tons (355,600 tonnes) of freight. By 1850 (in less than thirty years) there were over 6,000 miles (9,600km) of railways.

Chapter 6

The New Hartley Colliery Accident

The previous chapters have concentrated on the development of the railways, but what about mining in the area? Mining remained a notoriously dangerous occupation. Accidents occurred frequently and for a variety of reasons, from miners being crushed by mine carts and roof falls to flooding and explosions. Explosions had been a particular hazard in mines in North East England, since they were too deep for natural ventilation to keep the mines free from methane. Methane, or Fire-damp as it was frequently known, could be easily ignited. The invention of the safety lamp gave miners warning of its presence. Carbon Monoxide, also known as White-damp, was another problem. Miners used to take canaries with them which would continue to sing until Carbon Monoxide levels increased, giving the miners an early warning of its presence. However it was the effects of Stythe, also known as Choke-damp or Block-damp, a mixture of Carbon Dioxide and Nitrogen, that led to the deaths at Hartley, which then led to a change in the law (see below) and a change in the way the nation viewed miners and their families.

The original Hartley Pit, in south east Northumberland, was closed in 1844 when, having extended the workings towards the coast the mine was flooded by sea water. The following year a new pit was dug in the same area. This became the New Hartley Colliery which was known locally as the Hester Pit. Construction of the single shaft was led by William Coulson, the master sinker for Durham, and they reached the Low Main Seam on 29 May 1846. As both the Old Hartley Colliery and the new pit worked the coal towards the coast they encountered problems with flooding from the sea. Figure 75 might well be a section of part of this mine that is exposed in Hartley Bay. On one occasion the flooding was so great that the miners and pit ponies had to be evacuated from the pit as water rose 490 feet (149.3m) up the shaft!

It is probably this event that led to mining being abandoned for twelve years, until a powerful pumping engine was built at the surface. This was the largest pump engine in the coalfield and had been working for four (some sources say six) years prior to 1862 when, only a week before the accident, the bearings were changed. During this operation the beam slipped and fell on to the bearings 'with great force'. This may have produced the weakness that resulted in one of the biggest mining accidents the country has ever experienced.

Figure 75: Coal mine exposed along the coast at Hartley Bay. The hole represents a collapsing stall (a) (where the coal had been removed and subsequently back filled) with the supporting pillars (b) in tact on either side. The dashed lines indicate the sides of the pillars

It is worth covering the accident in some detail if only to give a feel for the dangers of mining, the devastation which accidents produce in mining families and communities, and the reaction locally and nationally of those directly and indirectly involved.

At about ten thirty on the morning of Thursday 16 January 1862 an accident occurred that sent shock waves across the country. The mine was extracting coal from three seams; the High Main which was 130 feet (39.6m) below the surface, the Yard Seam 390 feet (119m below) and the Low Main at 570 feet (174m) below. The mine was accessed through a single 12 foot (3.6m) diameter shaft which contained a Brattice (a wooden wall) that divided the shaft in two (figure 76). The downcast side was used to transport coal and miners between the coal seams and the surface in two, double-decked cages. The other side of the partition, the upside, was used for ventilation which was driven by a furnace in a small drift that joined the Yard Seam. The High Main Seam had an access to the surface and the Low Main was connected to the Yard Seam by an inclined drift (Tunnel). There was no connection between the Yard Seam and the High Main.

Why is the time important? The miners of the first shift that had gone down the mine at 1 o'clock (other sources quote 2:30am) in the morning were just about to be relieved by the miners that came in on the back shift at 9 o'clock. This meant that for a relatively short period of time almost two full shifts of miners were in the mine at the same time. Two sets of men had already been brought up to the surface and a third set was coming up in the cage when the arm of the pump engine broke and fell down the shaft. The broken section which comprised almost half of the arm and weighed around 20 tons (20.32 tonnes) was made of cast iron. As the broken arm fell down the shaft it completely smashed the brattice and the stone lining of the shaft, which hit the cage breaking two of the four support chains, throwing four men out and leaving four more hanging in the shattered cage. During the rescue of these four, one fell to his death. Once rescuers had reached the damaged cage around mid-night the other three were brought to surface. This included Thomas Watson, a local preacher who had climbed down the signal wires to try to reach the Yard Seam. When he found he could not reach it he climbed down the side of the shaft to two men who had fallen on to the debris blocking the shaft, and stayed and prayed with them until they died. He then climbed back up to a recess in the shaft and waited, along with those in the cage, to be rescued.

Figure 76: The capped mine shaft (in the foreground) and the base of the engine house (background) at New Hartley

The broken wood completely blocked the shaft about 33 feet (10m) above the Yard Seam, trapping 199 miners and boys underground. The broken pump arm meant that pumping stopped and the mine began to fill with water. It was assumed by those at the surface that the trapped miners, knowing what had happened, would make their way up from the Low Main to the Yard Seam which would be above any flooding.

A rescue mission was started immediately. This was led by William Coulson, the master sinker for Durham, who happened to be passing by the village at the time. News spread very quickly and miners, particularly very experienced miners, and rescue teams from all over the north east arrived on site as fast as they could get there. This allowed Coulson to pull together a very able team of miners, particularly sinkers (miners skilled in digging the shafts) with all skills necessary to rescue the trapped men and boys. Someone even suggested dropping the other half of the beam down the shaft to clear the blockage, but the idea was rejected.

Because of the cramped and dangerous conditions, only two men could work in the shaft at the same time. They were lowered by ropes down to the wreckage to clear it by hand in hour-long shifts. By the following afternoon they had cleared the debris to within 30 feet (9m) of the Furnace Drift. The rescuers could hear the trapped miners in the Yard Seam. Suddenly a section of the walls of the shaft collapsed further blocking access to the Yard Drift and narrowly missing the rescuers.

On Saturday morning the rescue party managed to reach and retrieve the bodies of four of the five men that had been killed in the shaft. The fifth body was recovered the following day. By then they had cleared another six feet (1.8m) of debris and rock, but then another even larger section of the walls of the shaft caved in, forming a cavity 30 feet (9m) across. The rescuers then had to shore up this section of the shaft in case it collapsed again. Further small failures occurred as they continued to remove the blockage. They were convinced that they could still hear the trapped miners on the Sunday morning, were sure that they were clear of the water and that there was no sign of any gas in the mine. By this time the colliery surgeon was extremely concerned about the welfare of those trapped. The men of the first shift had been down the pit for 89 hours and the back shift had been there for 81 hours. He was most concerned for the 50 boys that had been there for around 85 hours with little or no food or water.

By the Monday, five days after the accident, the rescue party was within 12 feet (3.6m) of the Furnace Drift when the Government Inspector of Mines arrived with yet another large group of experienced mining people. The colliery surgeon and a team of other doctors had been waiting at the pit head throughout this time, ready to deal with the injured as soon as they were brought to the surface.

It was reported in the *Times* on Monday 20 August 1862 that nearly the whole working male population of the village was trapped in the mine and that one lady had her husband and six children, and a boy they had been looking after, trapped in there.

On the Tuesday several rescuers were overcome by Carbon Monoxide (White-damp) and had to be rescued themselves. This had been produced by the buried furnace and the rocks that had been burning around it. It was then decided that further rescue work could not continue until the Brattice had been rebuilt to allow the pit to be ventilated again. This had been finished by Wednesday afternoon, six days after the accident, the same day that Queen Victoria sent the following telegram to the colliery from Osborne House on the Isle of Wight:

> General Grey, Osborne, to the viewer of New Hartley Colliery, Shields.
>
> The Queen is most anxious to hear that there are hopes of saving the poor people in the colliery, for whom her heart bleeds.

That morning three sinkers had reached the Furnace Drift, where they found evidence that the trapped miners had tried to relight it. It was to become clear at this point that everyone in the mine had died. The rescue party was then overcome by gas and had to return to the surface. Realising that gas had penetrated the Yard Seam, further rescue work was suspended until the shaft had been properly secured to avoid any further deaths or injuries.

Queen Victoria sent another telegram later that day:

> Sir C. Phipps to Messrs Carr Brothers [one of the mine owners] Hartley, Newcastle.
>
> The Queen has been deeply afflicted by the dreadful news from Hartley. Her Majesty feels the most sincere sympathy for the poor widows and orphans. What is doing for them? I write by to-night's post.

Mr Forster sent the following reply:

> Measures have been adopted for the immediate relief of the poor people. A public meeting is to be held tomorrow at Newcastle for forming a permanent relief fund. There are 406 women and children left destitute.

A further telegram from Osborne House arrived later on the 23 August:

> Sir, The Queen, in the midst of her own overwhelming grief, has taken the deepest interest in the mournful accident at Hartley, and up to the last had hoped that at least a considerable number of the poor people might have been recovered alive. The appalling news since received has afflicted the Queen very much.
>
> Her Majesty commands me to say that her tenderest sympathy is with the poor widows and mothers, and that her own misery only makes her feel the more for them.

In was about 11 o'clock on Saturday 25 August that the rescuers first entered the Yard Seam. The first two people to enter the shaft were Joseph Humble the mine manager and a Mr Hall, manager of a nearby pit. The first bodies they found were two brothers who appeared to have collapsed on to the ashes of the furnace. It is thought that they were the last two to die. The bodies of the rest of the miners, boys and a pit pony were found lining the sides of the drift. Humble's words reflect his feelings on seeing the miners:

> Oh, my men, my canny men, they would have done ought for me and

there they all are lying dead and cold.

Hall and Humble were then brought back up the shaft having been overcome by grief and gas, and other rescuers went into the Yard Seam. The following description, taken from an eye-witness by John Chapman, published by T. Mason in *The Science and Art of Mining* (1911) gives a very good description of the scene that confronted the rescuers:

> All around the entrance to the Yard Seam, and beside the furnace – the deadliest place in that awful catacomb – men and boys were sitting and lying in various attitudes, so natural in appearance as to seem asleep or resting. One property of the poisonous gas to which the men and boys had succumbed is that it preserves the natural appearance of the person and prevents rigidity.
>
> One little fellow, a driver named Cousins sat with his eyes wide open and bright, gazing wistfully in the direction of the shaft. So natural did the lad appear that one of the party of workers went to him and gave a slight shake, thinking he must surely be alive.
>
> Alas! Poor fellow! An earthquake's shock would not of arose him: his was a sleep that knows no waking, another pathetic sight was a man sitting with his stepson, a trapper boy, upon his knee, his arms clasped tight round the boy's slight form, and the boy's arms were round his father's neck.
>
> The bodies of the men and boys were found lying in three rows, all quiet and placid, as if sleeping off a heavy day's work.
>
> Boys were lying with their hands on the shoulders of their fathers, and one poor fellow had his arms clasped around the neck of his brother.

Evidence was found that the miners knew that they would not survive long enough to be rescued. They found a small memorandum book detailing a prayer meeting and an inscription on a shot-box where a hewer had scratched a message to his wife, "Friday afternoon, my dear Sarah, I leave you."

The accident had major consequences on New Hartley and the surrounding villages. At the time of the accident the population was thought to be 597. There were 140 children aged between 4 and 12 of which 105 were left without a father after the accident. 42 of the 204 people killed were under 16 years of age including two ten year olds and the oldest person to die was 70. It took 17 hours to bring all of the bodies to the surface. The coffins containing the bodies were then taken to their homes and laid out ready for the funeral.

Local, regional and national interest in the accident had reached such a level that on Sunday 26 there were approximately 60,000 people (some sources quote 20,000) in the village and along the route taken by the funeral procession to the local church, St Alban's at Earsdon, four miles (6.4km) away. So many people had been killed that the grave yard had to be expanded on to land donated by the Duke of Northumberland.

150 bodies were buried at Earsdon, the others going to Horton and Cramlington. The funeral procession was so long that the first coffins were being buried at Earsdon before others had left New Hartley.

Reaction to the disaster was swift. The jury at the inquest in to the deaths returned its verdict on 6 February. One of the major concerns was the single shaft:

> The jury cannot close this painful inquiry without expressing their stirring opinion of the imperative necessity that all working collieries should have at least a second shaft or outlet, to afford the workmen the means of escape should any obstruction take place.

This led to the passing of an Act of Parliament on 7 August 1862 which made it compulsory that all new mines should have two shafts and that existing mines would have to sink a second shaft by 1 January 1865.

It would be interesting to speculate on the works of James Mather who was born in Newcastle in 1799. Had he succeeded in his efforts to introduce improved safety measures in mines the death toll may not have been so great. He was an important campaigner for mining safety who felt that reporting mining accidents first-hand would provoke the government in to changing the law. He was instrumental in getting a general inquiry committee to look into the mining accident at St. Hilda's Pit in South Shields in 1839 where 50 boys and men died. By 1845 the committee had made several recommendations, including less reliance on the use of safety lamps and a requirement for mines to have two shafts to increase ventilation. If the two attempts to introduce mining bills into Parliament in 1847 and 1848 had not been defeated by powerful mining interests New Hartley would have had a second shaft!

Parliament did however set up a House of Lords Committee that led to the Mines Safety Act of 1850, which established the need for an Inspector of Mines and a voluntary safety code. This changed after the 1860 accident at Burradon in which 72 people were killed, when the number of mine inspectors was increased, but there was still no legal requirement for two shafts.

Some changes designed to improve the safety of miners had already been introduced, in addition to the safety lamp. A change in the law in 1834 meant that miners had to travel in cages in mine shafts rather than ladders, chains or ropes. The 1842 Mines Act banned women and children under 10 from working in mines, although they could be employed at the surface. Until then children as young as five or six could be employed down mines!

Following the Mine Inspection Act of 1852 the North of England Institute of Mining Engineers was formed and Nicholas Wood became its first president. He started a campaign to persuade the University of Durham to set up the College of Physical Science in Newcastle which eventually became the University of Newcastle.

After the Hartley accident a Relief Committee was formed to raise funds to provide money to look after the families of miners killed in accidents. This is thought to have reached £80,000 and included a £200 donation from Queen Victoria and £300 from the Duke of Northumberland. This led to the setting up of the Northumberland and Durham Miners Permanent Relief Fund on 12 February 1862. A weekly contribution for every miner was then made to the fund to provide money for an allowance for miner's widows and a small pension for retired miners.

ERECTED
TO THE MEMORY, OF THE 204 MINERS, WHO LOST THEIR
LIVES IN HARTLEY PIT, BY THE FATAL CATASTROPHE
OF THE ENGINE BEAM BREAKING, 16 JANUARY 1862.

J. AMOUR.	AGED 13	C. WANLESS.	AGED 20
R. AMOUR.	AGED 11	T. WANLESS.	AGED 19
J. TERNENT.	AGED 11	J. WANLESS.	AGED 14
C. TERNENT.	AGED 15	W. JACK.	AGED 24
W. PAPE.	AGED 11	W. CLEDSON.	AGED 71
T. SHARP.	AGED 18	W. CLEDSON	AGED 43
H. SHARP.	AGED 14	C. CLEDSON.	AGED 11
A. ELLIOTT.	AGED 9	T. CLEDSON	AGED 36
C. SHARP.	AGED 19	T. CLEDSON.	AGED 16
G. SHARP.	AGED 15	W. LIDDLE	AGED 10
J. SHARP.	AGED 13	W. LIDDLE.	AGED 17
J. BEWICK.	AGED 31	J. LIDDLE.	AGED 15
J. BEWICK.	AGED 32	J. LIDDLE.	AGED 16
R. BEWICK.	AGED 30	T. LIDDLE	AGED 13
T. ROBINSON.	AGED 12	G. LIDDLE	AGED 16
T. DAWSON.	AGED 19	J. LIDDLE.	AGED 11
J. DAWSON.	AGED 12	T. LIDDLE	AGED 11
A. RICHARDSON.	AGED 22	T. LIDDLE.	AGED 18
J. JOHNSON.	AGED 11	T. LAWS.	AGED 21
R. JOHNSON.	AGED 12	G. LAWS.	AGED 21
T. COAL.	AGED 37	W. LOUGE.	AGED 30
T. CHAMBERS.	AGED 55	J. LONG.	AGED 15
C. CHAMBERS.	AGED 19	R. LONG.	AGED 17
J. HUMBLE.	AGED 27	M. MURRAY.	AGED 28
W. DIXON.	AGED 34	R. MURLEY	AGED 2

Figure 77: One face of the memorial to the accident which lists the names and ages of the victims

Figure 78: The plaque commemorating the accident at the mine site.

The pit never reopened. About ten years later the Seaton Delavel Collieries sank two shafts, one at Melton and the other at Hastings which was less than half a mile (0.8km) from the Hester Pit. This mine reached the Yard Seam in 1877 and, once it was drained they broke through to the Hester Pit in 1900 where they found coal trucks full of coal left where the miners had abandoned them at the time of the accident 38 years before.

A monument was built in the church yard at Earsdon that records the names of everyone that was killed (figure 77) which really brings home the scale of the disaster. When you look at the lists of all 204 names you realise how devastating it must have been, with as many as seven people listed who were probably from the same family. The top of the shaft was capped and now sits in amongst two rows of houses (figure 76) as a stark reminder of the price paid by miners. There is also a plaque (figure 78) commemorating the event which was laid by Joe Gormley in 1976 when he was president of the National Union of Mineworkers. The small park around the shaft has a simple serenity which belied the fear, death and suffering that must have taken place there all those years ago.

Chapter 7

Coal Mining: 1850-1950

In 1787 there were around 7,000 miners employed in mines in the North-East of England. By 1810 this had grown to about 10,000 and by 1919 it had further increased to 223,000, 154,000 of whom worked in mines in County Durham.

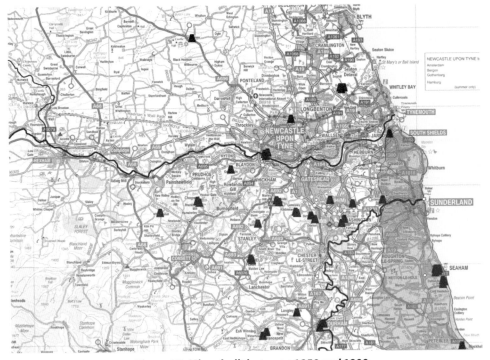

Figure 79: Mines built between 1850 and 1900

By 1923 there were 170,000 miners in the county. Figure 79 shows that, this period saw the continued development of collieries on the concealed coalfield, but with the establishment of the new railways mining was still expanding to the south and west of Durham City.

Mining on the exposed coalfield owned by the Londonderrys began to run down, partly because the coal was running out, but also partly due to the depression of the early 1890s. Framwellgate, the Penshaw collieries, Plain Pit at Rainton, Pittington and Belmont were either closed or sold to other people. The Old Durham Colliery closed in 1892, Adventure in 1893 and Rainton Meadows, Nicholson's, Alexandria and Lady Seaham closed in 1896. Rainton Meadows and Adventure were then reopened by other people and Rainton Meadows remained open until 1923. Adventure eventually closed in 1978!

Following the opening of the Monkwearmouth and Seaham collieries a number of large, new mines were constructed along the Durham coast to extract coal from under the sea (figure 80).

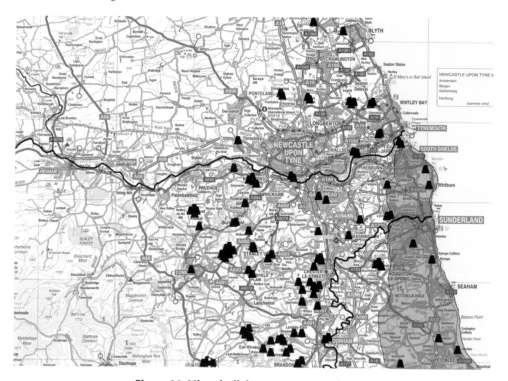

Figure 80: Mines built between 1900 and 1950

Work started on the shafts for Easington Colliery in 1899 and the mine produced its first coal on 15 September 1910. Dawdon Colliery was developed to reduce the cost of coal being mined out under the sea to the south-east from the Seaham Colliery. Two shafts were dug on the cliffs at Noses Point. To counteract the problems encountered whilst digging through the Magnesian Limestone and Yellow Sands at other pits, the walls of the shafts were frozen to lock in the water until they could be lined. This became the standard approach for all of the new mines. Work began in March 1900 and the first coal was produced in October 1907. Construction of the first of the three shafts at Horden also started in 1900 with the first coal being produced in 1904. For most of its life, Horden was the largest mine in Britain. The first shaft at Blackhall Colliery, which was used to supply fresh water to the village, and the first colliery shaft were both started in 1909. The first coal was produced in 1913. Blackhall was one of the last of the mines developed to mine out under the sea and appears to have been the first colliery to dump all of its spoil in the sea. The other coastal mines then followed suit. Vane Tempest Colliery was built to extract coal from under the sea to the north east of Seaham. This was an area that existing collieries could not reach. It had two shafts, Vane which began construction in 1924 and Tempest which started in 1926.

Following the high demand for coal during the Second World War, production decreased and mines began to close. After nationalisation in 1947, the number of miners in Durham fell to 108,000 working in 127 collieries (some sources say 134 mines). Between 1950 and 1970 approximately 100 mines closed. Closures continued throughout the 80s and 90s until Wearmouth Colliery, the last operational mine in the county, closed in 1994.

Chapter 8

What We Can See Today

The initial answer would appear to me not very much! Most of the preserved artefacts relate to the railways. These include Causey Arch, and the Tanfield and Bowes railways, which can all rightly be regarded as being of world importance. Beyond those though we have early steam engines preserved at the museums at Darlington, Silverlink and Shildon.

Although most of the original pit villages still exist, many are really only a shadow of their former selves and have changed very little over the last hundred years. In many former pit villages you can still see where the pit used to be and local street names still record specific functions and sometimes personalities associated with mining. You can take a walk around part of the abandoned pit village of Houghall Colliery in the woods at Houghall College, Durham (figure 81).

Here you can still see the layout of part of the village which includes floors, walls, back yards and even the steps of some of the houses. In fact, if you look carefully you can still make out the boundaries of some of the gardens and find blackberry bushes etc. which it appears the miners, or their families were growing! You can also walk along some of the track embankments and around the foundations and occasional floors of some of the 153 pit houses and see the tops of at least two covered mine shafts surrounded by small pit heaps. The colliery opened in 1840 and the miners and their families may well have original lived in wooden shacks until brick houses were built in 1860. The village was finally demolished in 1955.

Figure 81: Houghall Colliery and village. To the right is a view looking along a path with front door steps belonging to some of the houses. Above shows one of the colliery mine shafts

Beamish Open Air Museum is probably the best place to be able to 'get a feel' for mining and the early railways in this area. It has an adit/drift mine that visitors can go into which represents the earlier methods of mining, and a Whin Gin (figure 82). This was a horse-powered winding system which raised coal to the surface in large baskets called corves that were attached to a rope. They have also built a short section of a wooden waggonway down-slope from the mine site (figure 83) which offers a good comparison to the iron waggonway beside the gin (figure 84). Adjacent to the adit/drift they have re-built a shaft mine, engine house and winding gear (figure 85) together with its spoil tip and railway that shows how mining continued to develop.

Figure 82: A reproduction of a Whin Gin mine

Figure 83: (Above left) The reproduction wooden waggonway adjacent to the Whin Gin at Beamish Open Air Museum

Figure 84: (Above) The 1825 waggonway which has been built as part of the 1825 Locomotion/Stephenson Project

Figure 85: (Left) The steam powered shaft mine at Beamish Open Air Museum

The museum has also reconstructed elements of a mining village adjacent to the two mines which shows life in a 'typical' mining village. Two other areas of the museum show the development of the railways. They have rebuilt an old engine shed and a waggonway (figure 84) to represent the railways in 1825 on which working replicas of the Steam Elephant, Puffing Billy and Locomotion are operated. This can then be compared to the 1913 station and railway on the other side of the museum site.

But what of the waggonways? Generally these are poorly represented. There is a map of the one at Killingworth next to Dial Cottage and maps and signs tell you about Stephenson, Hackworth and the others who lived and worked in Wylam. There is also a footpath along the line of the Wylam Waggonway from the river at Wylam (close to the site of the original mine) to the Tyne Riverside Country Park at Newburn. This passes the cottage where George Stephenson was born. Many of the waggonways still exist in the form of paths or bridleways which can be seen quite clearly on maps and aerial photographs. The same is true for the routes of many of the early railways which criss-cross the region.

Preservation of our mining heritage is not so obvious. Apart from the 'F' Pit Museum (figure 86) in Washington, various winding gear wheels, the occasional cauldron or a mining-related sculpture, and the miners' cage at Easington (figure 87) there is little else left. A number of sites have notice boards, such as Dawdon and Blackhall Colliery which give details of the mines, but the sites themselves have largely been cleared of all evidence of mining apart from the occasional gas vent and various buildings that have been abandoned or are being used for other purposes. There are engine sheds and other buildings which are still in use at some sites such as Hetton and Herrington and a couple of old steam engine houses such as those at Gateshead and Haswell (figure 88), but most sites have been cleared.

Figure 86: The 'F' Pit Museum in Washington

Figure 87: Right is a photograph of the time line at Easington Colliery which shows the history of the colliery on one side of the path and the geological sequence on the other. Left is a photograph of the mine cage that is preserved at the top of the hill

Figure 88: Above is an old engine house at Gateshead and right is the one at Haswell that has been preserved as a memorial to all the miners killed in the 1844 accident

At Easington, the site of one of the last mines in the area, a path (figure 87) has been laid which is the same length, 1,588 feet (174m) as the depth of one of the mine shafts. One side of the path is marked with the geological sequence down the shaft and the other side shows a time line for the pit.

What does this show? Even though most of the mine sites have been cleared and many have been built on, there still a lot of things to see if you look carefully. A gas vent marks the location of one of the mine shafts at Dawdon (figure 89). Similar gas vents can be found outside the Stadium of Light in Sunderland (figure 90), at Easington (figure 91) and even in an apparently ordinary field at Fatfield (figure 92).

Figure 89: (Above) A gas vent on a capped shaft at Dawdon Colliery
Figure 90: (Right) Gas vents beside the Stadium of Light, Sunderland

Figure 91: A gas vent on a capped shaft at Easington

Figure 92: A gas vent in a field close to the site of Chartershaugh Colliery in Fatfield

There are 'monuments' to mining found at various locations around the region such as the mining waggons that have been used as flower tubs on a roundabout on the A693 at Stanley (figure 93), the wagon at Elemore (figure 94) or the pit pony and waggon statue in the roundabout on the A181 next to Thornley Hall (figure 95) and even a large section of rock which is supposed to represent a lump of coal at Ushaw Moor (figure 96). There is another small coal waggon outside the mining cottages along the sea front in Seaham (figure 97).

Figure 93: Waggons at Stanley

Figure 94: A waggon at Elemore

Figure 95: A pit pony statue near Thornley

Figure 96: A 'block of coal' at Ushaw Moor

Figure 97: A waggon at Seaham

Winding wheels form one of the most popular artefacts used to commemorate mining. Below are is selection of photographs (figures 98 to 110) of the wheels that have been preserved around the coalfield.

 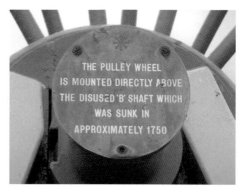

Figure 98: A winding wheel at Albany, Washington

Figure 99: A winding wheel at the Stadium of Light, Sunderland

Figure 100: A winding wheel at Seaham Harbour

Figure 101: A winding wheel at Burnhope

Figure 102: A winding wheel at South Hetton

Figure 103: A winding wheel at Blackhall

Figure 104: A winding wheel at Bear Park

Figure 105: A winding wheel at Easington
that has been used in a flower bed

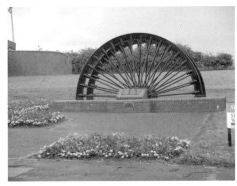

Figure 106: A winding wheel at Shotton

Figure 107: A winding wheel at Wheatley Hill

Figure 108: A winding wheel at West Stanley

Figure 109: A winding wheel at Blyth

Figure 110: A winding wheel at Ryton

One other 'iconic' symbol, the Davy Lamp, that is closely associated with coal mining has been used to commemorate our mining heritage, One has been included with other artefacts in a mining diorama at Sacriston (figure 111), a large replica can be found at Craghead (figure 112) and another one stands outside the Stadium of Light in Sunderland (figure 113).

Figure 111: (Above) The diorama at Sacriston
Figure 112: (Right) A Davy Lamp replica at Craghead

This example has a continuous flame which was used to light the first of the torches that were carried around the country to light beacons celebrating the Millennium. Coal wagons can be found at a number of locations, such as the one at East Hartford (figure 114).

Figure 113: (Left) A replica of a Davy lamp outside the Stadium of Light
Figure 114: (Above) A waggon at East Hartford close to the route of the Plessey Waggonway which is full of 'coal'

The North East's Black Beaches

One of the interesting remnants of coal mining in the Durham Coalfield are the famous black beaches along the Durham coast, which have a rather gentle and benign image. Unfortunately the black beaches are not the only legacy along the coastline that we have from mining. Even though all of the large collieries have gone (figure 115), their sites cleared, and in a number of cases been built on, we still live with their waste.

Figure 115: Easington Colliery shortly after its closure

Dawdon, Horden, Easington and Blackhall, four of the six large collieries along the coast, used to dump all of their spoil in the sea. When they first opened this did not pose a problem, because they were producing waste at a rate that the sea could easily remove and disperse. As production increased and the volume of spoil being dumped in the sea topped 2.4 million tonnes a year in the 1950s it became too large for natural coastal processes to remove and a series of artificial beaches began to form. It is estimated that the six collieries dumped between 120 and 150 million tonnes of waste on the coast.

The 'Blast Beach' (thought to be named after an old iron works that used to exist at Noses Point) at Dawdon was almost 400m wide and up to 10m deep (figure 116). Most of the collieries used aerial ropeways to carry the waste to the sea. As production increased these were replaced by conveyors which could transport significantly larger quantities of spoil. It is not appropriate or necessary to go in to the nature of the spoil or the damage it did to the coastline. It is probably sufficient to remember that the beaches were used as the bleak landscape in the third *Alien* film!

Figure 116: Two views of the 'Blast Beach' at Dawdon

These were regarded as 'a blight' on the coast, particularly as the 12km of coast between Ryhope and Trimdon was designated a Heritage Coastline in 2001. The National Trust together with a number of other organisations such as Durham County Council, Easington District Council, the Countryside Agency and the Environment Agency initiated the Black Beach Project designed to clean up the coastline as part of a larger £10 million 'Turning the Tide' project.

This involved the removal of 1.3 million tonnes of waste from the beaches (figure 117) and cliff-top spoil heaps were spread over the colliery sites at Horden and Easington and then covered with soil. Removal of all of the waste was 'deemed impractical'. It is thought that the remaining spoil will be removed by the sea over a five-to-ten year period.

Figure 117: Three views of Easington beach prior to (above, left), during (above) and following (left) the Black Beaches Project

You might well ask why this has been included in a book about the development of coal mining and railways in the region. The 'Blast Beach' at Dawdon and the beach at Easington both comprise large quantities of colliery waste. This is industrial heritage!

If you visit the 'Blast Beach' (figure 116), particularly at the northern end close to Noses Point, you can see different aspects of mining in the layers of spoil (figure 118). It effectively holds a potted history of the mine. At the base of the beach you find pit props (figure 119), nails, sections of track and occasionally things such as a miner's boot! It could almost be regarded as a time capsule. The level of pollution is evident from the lack of vegetation on most of the beach and the iron staining in the pools of water along the base of the cliffs (figure 120).

Figure 118: The different layers of waste which comprise the 'Blast Beach'

Figure 119: Pit props near the base of the 'Blast Beach'

Figure 120: One of the iron-rich ponds at the back of the 'Blast Beach'

The beach at Easington has even more interesting things to look at. There is a layer of rock towards the north end of the beach which is exposed at low tide that contains old wheels, railways tracks, nuts and bolts that are literally encased in the rock. If they were shells or bones you would regard them as fossils. In fact, that is exactly what they are. Geologically they would be regarded as trace fossils, something left behind which shows that an organism (in this case human) has been there. If you look carefully, all of the objects are not lying on the surface of the rock; they are part of it (figure 121). The rock has formed around them. This layer of rock is extremely important because it really is another time capsule. If you go to see it treat it with as much care and regard as you would any other monument to our mining heritage because it encapsulates some of the nitty-gritty, everyday objects of coal mining in the Durham Coalfield.

Figure 121: Four different views of the wheels, rails, nuts, bolts and nails that have been 'fossilised' in part of the beach at Easington

With the closure of Ellington Colliery (figure 122) in January 2005 coal mining ceased in the region and we lost our last direct link to an industry that literally put the North East on the map. Why is this important? Many children today do not know what coal looks like! They have little idea of where it comes from and even less about the process of getting it out of the ground. Following closure the Ellington Colliery site was cleared for re-development. Should it have gone the same way as all of the others or should it have been preserved in some way?

Figure 122: Ellington Colliery shortly before it closed in January 2005

Fortunately there is a colliery that has to a large extent been preserved; its name is Woodhorn (figure 123). They began digging the first shaft on 16 May 1894 and produced their first coal in February 1898. A second shaft was added around 1897 and the mine produced coal until it closed in 1981. It first opened as a museum in 1989. It then closed for refurbishment and opened again at the end of October 2006. It was reported that in the first week after it reopened over 10,000 people visited the museum. Some of the site has been cleared but the majority of the mine buildings including both heapstead (the building around the top of the mineshaft containing headgear and engine houses), jack and crab engine houses, stables and workshops have been preserved, together with much of their equipment (figures 124 to 126). There is also a large, purpose-built visitor's centre that depicts various aspects of the lives of the miners and their families in chronological order.

Figure 123: (Above) The Headgear and associated buildings at Woodhorn Colliery Museum.
Figure 124: (Right) Inside the heapstead at Woodhorn Colliery Museum

Figure 125: (Above) The Jack engine at Woodhorn Colliery Museum

Figure 126: (Right) The ventilation fan at Woodhorn Colliery Museum

The buildings that are open to the public allow you to see many of the 'workings' of the mine which do not exist at Beamish Open Air Museum. It is hardly surprising that the Woodhorn Colliery Museum gives a better sense of the layout of a colliery and how it worked although, to some extent, it feels a bit too clean and tidy whereas the mine at Beamish gives more of a feel of the grimy, day-to-day look and feel of a working mine and tries to cover mining in a wider context, especially through the miners' cottages, chapel and railway. Apart from that Beamish also gives you the chance to go into a mine and get some idea of the working conditions underground. Therefore if you want to be able to see something of the life of coal miners and their families you should try to visits to both museums.

The other museum that is worth visiting to see mines, transport and industry together is the Blists Hill Open Air Museum at Ironbridge, Coalbrookdale, in Shropshire. This is a most fantastic place to visit especially when you go to all the museums in the Iron Bridge Gorge World Heritage site and see that there was so much going on in such a relatively small area that changed the world.

Although I have said that there is little in the way of officially preserved buildings and sites related to our mining heritage we have a number of museums which contain important parts of our railway heritage. These, including the National Railway Museum out-station at Shildon (as well as the main museum in York), the railway museum in Darlington, the Stephenson Museum at Silverlink, as well as the museums and working railways at Bowes and Tanfield.

Having said that, although much of the route of the historic 1822 Hetton-le-Hole to Sunderland line has been preserved as footpaths and bridleways there is little apart from three signs at Hetton, the base of Copt Hill and Farringdon (see figure 54) and the blue plaque in Hetton (figure 127). There appears to be no other information along the route, particularly where it passes through Sunderland. There is stylised metal portrait (figure 128) in the road embankment beside the roundabout where Silksworth Lane crosses Essen Way.

Figure 127: The 'blue plaque' outside the Methodist church in Hetton-le-Hole which is beside the route of the 1822 railway line

Figure 128: The stylised Hetton engine beside the route of the Hetton line where it crosses the Essen Way in Sunderland

The route then continues as a footpath past 'The Barnes' pub until it crosses the A183 Chester Road, where the base of the bridge still exists (figure 129), before passing through the grounds of the University of Sunderland Precinct halls of residence and crossing the Metro Railway (figure 130). It then continues until the route reaches the site of the coal staithes on the River Wear at Ayre's Quay (figure 131). The original route of tracks to the staithes were located at the top of the bank to the left of the photograph and can still be seen, even though the area is completely overgrown.

Figure 129: (Above Left) The base of the bridge where the Hetton line crosses over the A183, Chester Road in Sunderland
Figure 130: (Above Right) The route of the Hetton line over the Metro line behind the University of Sunderland's Precinct halls of residence
Figure 131: (Left) The end of the line, where the route of the Hetton line reaches the River Wear at Ayres Quay in Sunderland. The footpath in the foreground goes along the bases of the Hetton Staithes

It really is a shame that such an important part of the world's industrial history apparently passes without recognition through the centre of the city! If there were no other signs marking the route there should be a plaque on the walls of the bridge at Chester Road and a notice board could be placed either at the top of the embankment at Ayre's Quay or on the footpath which passes by the walls of the staithes. These could be used to show the route and explain the historic importance of this railway, not only to the region or even the country but as a globally-important industrial achievement. This is the line that turned a good idea into a fully operational and very successful railway that proved that steam power could be used on an industrial scale, and it deserves more recognition!

If you are like me you often drive past buildings without realising what they are or how important they are. A classic example of this was 48 Bridge Street in Stockton (figure 61). I passed it whilst going to Yarm to photograph the George and Dragon (figure 60) and could honestly say that I did not even notice the building. It was not until I was searching for information on the pub that I came across a reference to St John's Well. If you look up St John's on a map you end up at Stockton Station. This seems logical until you start to look for the reported plaques. Having then asked directions from various people in Stockton town centre I was amazed to find that a building I had paid no regard to was so important!

Figure 128 shows another example of this, I must have driven around the roundabout hundreds of times but it was not until I actually walked along the route of the Hetton line that I discovered this portrait. I'm sure that there are plenty more discoveries to be made and I am sure that many people who read this book will be equally amazed to find out what is on their doorstep.

The Virtual World

If you want to find out more about mining or the development of the railways in the North East there are a wide variety of web sites that you can access. Many of the better ones belong to museums, tourism sites and local organisations. Probably the most comprehensive site for mining information and history is the Durham Mining Museum site (www.dmm.org.uk). This has a wealth of information on all types of mining in the county which is often a good starting point for your search; it will lead to a wide variety of interesting facts, figures and locations which will allow you to explore our heritage even further. The other useful site is www.geocities.com/waggonways which contains maps of the waggonways and collieries in this area and formed the basis of the waggonway maps included in this book.

I have not included a list of useful web sites as, on the basis of my past experience, these often change. There is nothing more irritating than looking up useful web sites that have been included in a book, only to find that many of them are no longer available!

Index